The Thorvaldsen Museum

Dear George,
    Hope this is what you
are looking for.
        Love.
            Sue   1998

D1004747

KØBENHAVN 1995

© Thorvaldsens Museum
Catalogue edited by Bjarne Jørnæs, Torben Melander and Anne Sophie
Urne on the basis of the catalogues in English (1961) and Danish (1975).
Translation by Ingeborg Nixon 1961. Revised in 1995.
Photos by Sophus Bengtsson, Jonals & Co., Lennart Larsen, Ole Woldbye.
Printed by F. Hendriksens Eftf. A/S, Copenhagen.
English translation of the chapter on the Antique Collection by
David Lalley 1995.
Grateful acknowledgement to *Konsul Georg Jorck og Hustru Emma Jorck's
Fond* for contributing to the revised catalogue.

Contents

On the cover: View of ground floor rooms. On the backcover: Detail of vault in room 3. Photo: Ole Woldbye.

Plan of the Thorvaldsen Museum

Ground Floor
Entrance Hall and Corridors: Thorvaldsen's works (plaster models).
Rooms 1-21: Thorvaldsen's works (marble versions).
The Christ Hall: Plaster models for Thorvaldsen's works in the
Church of Our Lady, Copenhagen.

First Floor
Corridors: Thorvaldsen's works (plaster models).
Rooms 22-30: Thorvaldsen's collection of paintings.
Room 33: Lecture Hall.
Rooms 35-40: Thorvaldsen's collection of antiquities.

Basement
Rooms 43-46: Thorvaldsen's clothes and personal relics. Sculptural
technique.
Room 49 and Corridors 62 and 63: Thorvaldsen's juvenilia, sketch
models and drawings.
Rooms 50-56: Exhibition Rooms.
Corridor 64: Plaster casts from ancient sculptures.
Photomontage with a presentation of Thorvaldsen's life and work.

The Thorvaldsen Museum

is the property of the City of Copenhagen. The inscription on the side of the building facing the palace church gives the following account of its origin:

Thorvaldsen decided in the year 1837 in Rome that his works, collections and fortune should go to his native city Copenhagen and that with them should be established a separate museum.

By means of contributions from King Frederik VI and King Christian VIII, from the City of Copenhagen and from fellow citizens of every rank the task was completed 1848.

The building was designed by the architect M. G. Bindesbøll, and erected under his direction. The work was begun in 1839. When the building had already taken shape the desire was voiced that in addition to housing Thorvaldsen's works and collections it should also be his final resting-place. When his consent had been given to this, a sunken burial chamber was built under the centre of the courtyard, decorated with white lilies on a blue ground.

Thorvaldsen's coffin was placed in it on September 6th 1848. The granite edging of the tomb bears the following inscription:

BERTEL THORVALDSEN
b. 19th November 1770, d. 24th March 1844

During Thorvaldsen's lifetime the facades of the building were of undecorated plaster. It was not until two years after his death that Bindesbøll suggested that they should be ornamented with a frieze of figures. The idea was Bindesbøll's; he is believed to have given instructions for the subjects of the figure scenes, and how they were to be placed on the walls. The composition and execution are the work of Jørgen Sonne, under whose direction the frieze was made in 1846-48 and 1850. The technique used is unusual, the murals being constructed of tinted cement plaster applied direct to the walls. The side facing the canal shows Thorvaldsen's arrival in Copenhagen in 1838. Facing the palace church is the frigate Rota, from which his works are being unloaded. The side facing the palace shows the transport of the works to the Museum. The decorations on the walls facing the courtyard were carried out during the summer and autumn of 1844. The bay-trees, oaks, and palms are the work of the landscape painter H. C. From, while the frieze with the chariot-driving genii is the work of the German sculptor Johann Scholl.

The bronze group above the main entrance – Victory reining in her horses - was presented by Christian VIII. It was modelled by H. W. Bissen, who used a sketch by Thorvaldsen for the figure of the goddess (A 48), and one of his models for the second horse from the left (A 125). The reliefs on the corner pilasters were carved in sandstone by Johann Scholl from models by H. E. Freund. They were originally partly painted.

For the ceiling decorations, which were inspired by antique models, Bindesbøll employed a number of artists and young academy students, of whom G. C. Hilker, Christen Købke, Jørgen Sonne and C. F. Sørensen are the best known. Bindesbøll was the moving spirit of the undertaking. His various helpers worked more or less independently under his leadership, and occasionally from his personal designs. His ability to guide and inspire them was legendary.

On September 17th 1848, the tenth anniversary of Thorvaldsen's return from Italy, the city council officially took over Thorvaldsen's art collections, and on the following day the Museum was opened to the public.

The Museum contains both Thorvaldsen's own works and his collections. The former consist of a large number of drawings, (some of which are exhibited in the basement), many sketch models, most of his original full-scale models, a number of casts, marbles made under his direction and finished by him, and marble copies made by various artists after his death.

Thorvaldsen's collections are very extensive, and provide interesting evidence of his wide artistic taste. They include works from ancient Egypt, antique glass, antique and oriental bronzes, Greek and Roman marbles, large collections of gems and coins, especially Greek, a fine collection of ancient vases, and various objects in terracotta. But the outstanding feature is the collection of paintings. Though it includes a few Renaissance paintings, the main emphasis is on the art of Thorvaldsen's own day, of which it gives an excellent impression. There are also important collections of watercolours, drawings, engravings, books, and casts of antique sculptures.

Thorvaldsen's Life

1770   Bertel Thorvaldsen born 19th November, son of Gotskalk
       Thorvaldsen, a woodcarver from Iceland, and Karen Dagnes
       from Jutland
1781   admitted to the Academy of Fine Arts, Copenhagen
1787   wins the Academy's Minor Silver Medal for a lifesize drawing
       of a male nude
1789   wins the Academy's Major Silver Medal for the relief *Cupid
       Resting* (A756)
1791   wins the Academy's Minor Gold Medal for the relief *Helio-
       dorus Driven out of the Temple* (A829)
1792   carves a wooden gateway relief, *Mounted Horseman* (A872)
       from a drawing by the Navy sculptor F. C. Willerup. Models
       the relief *Hercules and Omphale* (A749) as a companion piece
       to a relief by Johann Gottfried Schadow
1793   wins the Academy's Major Gold Medal for the relief *The
       Apostles Peter and John Healing a Lame Man* (A830). During
       the period up to 1796 executes a number of portrait medal-
       lions and drawings
1794   executes statues and reliefs (A757-758, Dep. 21-22) for Heir
       Presumptive Prince Frederik's palace at Amalienborg, from
       designs by N. A. Abildgaard, his teacher at the Academy
1795   wins the Academy's travelling scholarship. Models the bust of
       Prime Minister A. P. *Bernstorff* (A856)
1796   sails from Copenhagen 29th August, arrives 24th October in
       Malta
1797   leaves Malta 19th January, arrives in Naples via Palermo 1st
       February, and travels overland to Rome, arriving 8th March,
       a date later to be celebrated as Thorvaldsen's 'Roman birth-
       day'. Meets Georg Zoëga, a Danish archaeologist living in

Rome, finds a studio in the Via Babuino and reworks the bust *of A. P. Bernstorff* (A208)

1798   lives in the Via Sistina and forms a relationship with Anna Maria Uhden, née Magnani, married to the Prussian diplomat Wilhelm Uhden. Models the statuette *Bacchus and Ariadne* (A1)

1799   begins to copy antique sculpture in plaster (A54) and marble (A751, A759-761)

1800   starts work on a life-size statue of *Jason* (this clay model destroyed in 1802)

1801   models the statuette *Achilles and Penthesilea* (A 777)

1802   starts work on a new statue of Jason, more than life-size (A52)

1803   finds a studio by the Piazza Barberini. *Jason* cast in plaster at the request of the poetess Friederike Brun and a marble version comissioned by Thomas Hope. Models the relief *Briseis Led away from Achilles by Agamemnon's Heralds (A490)*

1804   moves into the Casa Buti in the Via Sistina. Models the statues *Bacchus*(A2) and *Ganymede* (A41). Spends the summer with Baron and Baroness Schubart at Montenero and makes portrait busts of them (A718-719). Becomes a member of the Academy of Art, Florence

1805   appointed member of and professor at the Academy of Fine Arts, Copenhagen. Spends the summer at Montenero. Models the statue *Apollo* (A3) and starts work on the reliefs for a *Font* for Brahetrolleborg Church (A555)

1806   works on the *Font* and models the statues *Hebe* (A37) and *Psyche with the Jar of Beauty* (A26) His son with Anna Maria Magnani, Carlo Alberto, is born

1807   comissioned to do *four reliefs* for C. F. Hansen's Christiansborg Palace in Copenhagen and models the group Cupid and *Psyche Reunited In Heaven* (A 28)

1808   models the statue *Adonis* (A53), commissioned in marble by Crown Prince Ludwig of Bavaria (later Ludwig I), and the reliefs *Hercules and Hebe* (A317), *Aesculapius and Hygieia* (A318) and possibly *Minerva and Prometheus* (A319) for Christiansborg Palace. Becomes a member of the Accademia di San Luca, the Roman academy of art, and carves, presumably for the occasion, the relief A *Genio Lumen* (A518)

1809 becomes executor of the estate of Georg Zoëga on the latter's death. Is commissioned to do *four statues* for the facade of Christiansborg Palace, a project only realized in Thorvaldsen's final years. Models the bust of *Ida Brun* (A218)

1810 models the last relief for Christiansborg Palace, *Jupiter and Nemesis* (A320), the relief *Caritas* ('Christian Love', A598), the *self-portrait bust* (A223), and presumably *Mars and Cupid* (A7), a reworking of a *Mars the Bringer of Peace* from 1808, now no longer extant.

1811 becomes a member of the art academies of Berlin and Milan. His son, Carlo Alberto, dies

1812 models the *Alexander Frieze* (A503) for the Quirinal Palace on the occasion of Napoleon's expected visit to Rome

1813 models two *Caryatids* (A55-56) for a monument to be erected in Warsaw commemorating Napoleon's alliance with Poland, later used for the Throne Room at Christiansborg Palace. Starts work on the statue of *Venus* (A12), completed in 1816. Elisa, his daughter with Anna Maria Magnani, born

1814 on the death of Baroness Schubart models a *tomb relief* (A618). Portrayed by C. W. Eckersberg (painting, Academy of Fine Arts, Copenhagen). Becomes a member of the Academy of Art, Munich

1815 models the statue of *Countess Osterman-Tolstoy* (A167) and the reliefs *Night* (A369), *Day* (A370) and *Priam Pleading with Achilles for the Body of Hector* (A492)

1816 starts work on the restoration of the antique pediment figures from Aegina for Ludwig of Bavaria, completed in 1817. Models the bust of *C. W. Eckersberg* (A224) and the statues *Ganymede Filling the Cup* (A43) and *Hebe* (A870)

1817 models the two statues of *Dancing Girls* (A178-179), *Ganymede with Jupiter's Eagle* (A45), A *Shepherd Boy* (A177) and the bust of *Lord Byron* (A257). Begins on *Cupid and the Graces* (A29), completed in 1819. Commissioned to do an equestrian statue of the Polish national hero Jozef Poniatowski

1818 models the statue *Mercury* (A5) and the portrait statue of

Princess Baryatinskaya (A172). Meets Miss Frances Mackenzie

1819   begins on preparations for the equestrian statue of *Poniatowski* (A249) and models the *Lucerne Lion* (A119). Becomes engaged to Miss Mackenzie, but breaks the engagement off shortly afterwards. Leaves Rome on the 14th of July and travels to Copenhagen by way of Switzerland, arriving on the 3rd of October. Starts on busts of the Danish Royal Family (A191-194)

1820   appointed titular Councillor of State. Works commissioned for the Church of Our Lady and Christiansborg Palace. Leaves Copenhagen on the 11th of August and travels through Poland, where the bust of *Alexander I* is modelled. Commissioned to do a monument to *Nicolaus Copernicus* (A113) and a tomb relief commemorating *Wlodzimierz Potocki* (A115). Arrives in Rome on the 16th December

1821   models the *Christ* statue (A82) and begins on the *statues of the apostles* (A86-104) and the pediment group *The Preaching of John the Baptist* (A59-70) for the Church of Our Lady, Copenhagen

1822   works on the equestrian statue of *Poniatowski* (A125-126) and models *Copernicus* (A113)

1823   models the relief *Cupid Received by Anacreon* (A415). Commissioned to do a sepulchral monument to *Pius* VII for St. Peter's in Rome. Becomes a member of the French Academy of Art

1824   begins on the sculptures for the papal monument. Commissioned to do a sepulchral monument to *Eugène de Beauharnais,* Duke of Leuchtenberg, for the Michaelskirche in Munich, unveiled in 1830

1825   models a *Recumbent Lion* (A122)

1826   Vice-Presidency of the Accademia di San Luca. Visited by Pope Leo XII in his studio

1827   holds the office of President of the Accademia di San Luca until the end of 1828. Completes model for equestrian statue of *Poniatowski* (A123). Models sketches for a *Triumphant Muse* (A49-50), statue of *Princess Caroline Amalie* (A164) and presumably *Angel Holding a Font* (A112) for the Church of Our Lady

1828   completes *Jason* in marble (A822) for Thomas Hope, 2 years after its commissioning

1829   commissioned to do a monument to *Lord Byron*

1830   goes on a journey to Munich and is commissioned to do an equestrian statue of *Maximilian I*, Elector of Bavaria, and a statue of *Friedrich Schiller*

1831   completes the model for the statue of *Byron* (A130) and the marble version of *Adonis* for Ludwig of Bavaria. Sepulchral monument to *Pius VII* unveiled in St. Peter's

1832   adopts his daughter Elisa and goes with her on a journey to Vicenza. Continues alone to Milan. Commissioned to do a statue of *Johann Gutenberg* for Mainz. His daughter marries Colonel Fritz Paulsen

1833   appointed Director of the Academy of Art in Copenhagen. Begins modelling *Maximilian I* (A128), completed in 1835, and delegates the realization of a sketch for *Gutenberg* (A117), to be modelled full-size by H. W. Bissen (A114). Portrayed by Horace Vernet

1834   plans for a Thorvaldsen Museum discussed in Copenhagen

1835   models a sketch for *Schiller* (A138), modelled in colossal size (A770) by Wilhelm Matthiä

1836   models the series of reliefs *The Ages of Man and the Seasons* (A642-645) and a statue of *Conradin* (A150). Receives a Medal of Honour from the Accademia di San Luca

1837   decides to will his works and collections to Copenhagen. A committee is set up in Copenhagen for the establishment of a Thorvaldsen Museum, and a collection is begun for this purpose. M. G. Bindesbøll works on designs for the Museum. Thorvaldsen given honorary citizenship of Mainz. Models statue of a *Young Girl Dancing* (A181) during a cholera epidemic in Rome and starts on sketches for *three series of reliefs* (A458-479, A 433-448 and A 532-547), which are modelled by Pietro Galli for the Palazzo Torlonia and completed in 1838. Negotiations begun about a *Goethe monument* in Frankfurt

1838   models the statue *Vulcan* (A9). Sails from Italy on the 8th of
       August with the frigate *Rota,* carrying a large portion of
       Thorvaldsen's works and collections. Appointed *Konferensraad*
       (an eminent honorary title). Arrives in Copenhagen on the
       17th of September and moves into the Academy Director's re-
       sidence at Charlottenborg. Given freedom of the City of
       Copenhagen on the 21st November. On the 5th December
       issues the official document giving his collections to the City.

1839   meets Baron and Baroness Stampe and models the bust of
       Adam Oehlenschläger (A226) on their estate, Nysø, along with
       the *Self-portrait* statue (A162). The statues of Christ and ten
       apostles in marble versions are installed in the Church of Our
       Lady, Copenhagen. Once Frederik VI has donated the site for
       the Museum building, and several architects have sent in
       ideas, M. G. Bindesbøll's design is chosen, and the work of
       building is begun. Thorvaldsen receives the Grand Cross of
       the Order of the Dannebrog. Frederik VI dies

1840   models the statue of *Christian IV* for the latter's chapel in
       Roskilde Cathedral and two *reliefs* depicting family life at
       Nysø (A636-637). Sends off two sketches of *Goethe* (A13940)
       to Frankfurt, but the commission is cancelled

1841   starts out on the 24th of May on a journey to Rome accom
       panied by the Stampe family, arriving on the 12th of Septem-
       ber. Given honorary citizenship of Stuttgart. In Rome models
       sketches for two statues of apostles, *Thaddaeus* (A106-107)
       and *Andrew* (A109) for the Church of Our Lady, to substitute
       for two statues done earlier

1842   reworks *Cupid and the Graces* (A31) and models the statues of
       Thaddaeus (A105) and *Andrew* (A108) in full-size versions.
       Leaves Rome at the beginning of October and arrives in
       Copenhagen on the 24th October. Visits his museum during
       building operations

1843   models the colossal *Hercules* (A14) and sketches for the statu-
       es of *Minerva* (A17-18), *Nemesis* (A19-19a) and *Aesculapius*
       (A20-21), all four intended for the facade of Christiansborg
       Palace in bronze, and later placed in Prince Jørgen's Court-
       yard between Christiansborg and the Thorvaldsen Museum

1844   begins work on the bust of *Luther* (A188). Dies in the Royal
       Theatre on the 24th of March. Lies in state in the assembly
       hall of Charlottenborg, and the funeral service is held on the
       30th of March in the Church of Our Lady

1848   Thorvaldsen's coffin is laid in the burial chamber in the
       Thorvaldsen Museum's courtyard on the 6th of September.
       The Museum is officially opened on the 17th of September,
       and opened to the public the next day

Catalogue

Catalogue of Thorvaldsen's Works

In the case of marbles known or believed to be executed under Thorvaldsen's direction, and possibly finished by him, his name has been added in brackets.

For the sculptures fixed to the walls or pedestals the position in the museum is mentioned.

A1 Bacchus and Ariadne
Statuette. Original plaster model. Rome 1798. H. 58,4 cm.

A2 Bacchus Statue.
First floor, northern corridor.
Original plaster model. Rome 1804. H. 140 cm.

A3 Apollo Statue
First floor, northern corridor.
Original plaster model. Rome 1805. H. 144 cm.

A4 Mercury about to Kill Argus
See A873.

A5 Mercury about to Kill Argus
Ground floor, southern corridor.
Statue. Original plaster model. Rome 1818. H. 174,5 cm. Marble version, see A873.

A6 Mars and Cupid
Ground floor, room 7.
Statue. Marble version of A7 (Rome, probably 1810) completed in 1862 by B. L. Bergslien under the supervision of H. W. Bissen. H. 247 cm.

A7 Mars and Cupid
Ground floor, southern corridor.
Statue. Original plaster model, Cupid a plaster cast. Rome, probably 1810. H. 241 cm. An adaptation of a statue of Mars the Bringer of Peace, modelled in 1808, known from an engraving in Ferdinando Mori: *Le Statue e li Bassirilievi del Cavaliere Alberto Thorvaldsen,* Rome 1811. Marble version, see A6.

A8 Vulcan
Ground floor, room 9.
Statue. Marble version of A9 (Rome 1838) completed in 1861 by B. L. Bergslien under the supervision of H. W. Bissen. H. 239 cm.

A9 Vulcan
Ground floor, southern corridor.
Statue. Original plaster model. Rome 1838. H. 241 cm. Marble version, see A8.

A10 Vulcan
Sketch model for A9. Plaster. Rome, probably 1838. H. 60 cm.

A11 Venus with the Apple Awarded by Paris
See A853.

A12 Venus with the Apple Awarded by Paris
First floor, southern corridor.
Statue. Original plaster model.
Rome 1813-16. H. 161 cm. Marble
version, see A853.

A13 Venus and Cupid
Statuette. Original plaster model.
Rome, probably about 1800.
H. 53,5 cm.

A14 Hercules
Main staircase.
Statue. Original,plaster model.
Copenhagen 1843. H. 388 cm. A
bronze cast in Prince Jørgen's
Courtyard at Christiansborg Palace,
Copenhagen .

A15 Hercules
Sketch model for A14. Plaster.
Copenhagen 1843. H. 67,5 cm.

A16 Hercules
First sketch model for A14. Plaster.
Copenhagen 1839. H. 59 cm.

A17 Minerva
Sketch model. Plaster. Copenhagen
1843. H. 70 cm. From this sketch
model H. W. Bissen modelled a colossal Minerva statue, a bronze cast
of which stands in Prince Jørgen's
Courtyard at Christiansborg Palace,
Copenhagen .

A18 Minerva
First sketch model for A17. Plaster.
Copenhagen 1839. H. 61 cm.

A19 Nemesis
Sketch model. Plaster. Copenhagen
1843. H. 66 cm. From this sketch
model H. W. Bissen modelled a colossal Nemesis statue, a bronze cast
of which stands in Prince Jørgen's
Courtyard at Christiansborg Palace,
Copenhagen.

A19a Nemesis
First sketch model for A19. Plaster.
Copenhagen 1839. H. 58 cm.

A20 Aesculapius
Sketch model. Plaster. Copenhagen
1843. H. 67,4 cm. From this sketch
model H. W. Bissen modelled a colossal Aesculapius statue, a bronze
cast of which stands in Prince Jørgen's Courtyard at Christiansborg
Palace, Copenhagen.

A21 Aesculapius
First sketch model for A20. Plaster.
Copenhagen 1839. H. 60 cm.

A22 Cupid Triumphant
First floor, southern corridor.
Statue. Plaster cast. The original
plaster model, Rome 1814. H. 146
cm. Marble version, see A804.

A23 Cupid Triumphant, Examining his Arrow
First floor, room 24.
Statue. Marble version of A24
(Rome 1823) executed 1845-54 by
J. Scholl. H. 145 cm.

A24 Cupid Triumphant, Examining his Arrow
First floor, southern corridor.
Statue. Plaster cast. An adaptation
of A22. Rome 1823. H. 143,5 cm.
Marble version, see A23.

A25 Psyche with the Jar of Beauty
See A821.

A26 Psyche with the Jar of Beauty
First floor, northern corridor.
Statue. Original plaster model.
Rome 1806. H. 131,7 cm. Marble
version, see A 821.

A27 Cupid and Psyche Reunited in Heaven
Ground floor, room 2.
Statue. Marble version of A28
(Rome, probably 1807) executed in
1861 by Christian Freund under
the supervision of H. W. Bissen.
H. 135 cm.

A28 Cupid and Psyche Reunited in Heaven
First floor, northern corridor.
Statue. Cupid a plaster cast, Psyche
an original plaster model. Rome,
probably 1807. H. 134,5 cm.
Marble version, see A27.

A29 Cupid and the Graces
Statue. Original plaster model.
Rome 1817-18. H. 171 cm. Marble
version, see A894.

A30 The Graces
Sketch model for A29. Plaster.
Rome 1817. H. 58 cm.

A31 The Graces with Cupid's Arrow, and Cupid Playing a Lyre
Ground floor, room 18.
Statue. Marble version of A32
(Rome 1842) executed in 1864 by
Christian Freund under the super-
vision of H. W. Bissen H. 172,5
cm.

A32 The Graces with Cupid's Arrow, and Cupid Playing a Lyre
First floor, northern corridor.
Statue. Plaster cast. An adaptation
of A29. Rome 1842. H. 172,5 cm.
Marble version, see A31.

A33 Cupid Playing a Lyre
First floor, room 27.
Statue. Marble version of A786
(Rome 1819), probably executed in
1836 in Rome by J. Scholl.
H. 58,6 cm.

A34 Cupid Playing a Lyre
See A786.

A35 Cupid Standing with his Bow
See A819.

A36 Cupid Standing with his Bow
First floor, southern corridor.
Statue. Plaster cast. An adaptation
of A173. Rome, probably 1819.
H. 100,5 cm. Marble version, see
A819.

A37 Hebe
First floor, southern corridor.
Statue. Original plaster model.
Rome 1816. H. 153 cm. Marble
version, see A874. See also A870.

A38 Hebe
See A874.

A39 Hebe
Statue. Reworked plaster cast.
Rome 1816. H. 153 cm. Marble
version, see A874. See also A870.

A40 Ganymede Offering the Cup

See A854.

A41 Ganymede Offering the Cup

First floor, northern corridor.
Statue. Plaster cast. The original plaster model, Rome 1804. H. 135,7 cm. Marble version, see A854.

A42 Ganymede Filling the Cup

Ground floor, room 1.
Statue. Marble version (Thorvaldsen) of the original plaster model executed in 1816 in Rome. H. 135,5 cm. See A43.

A43 Ganymede Filling the Cup

First floor, northern corridor.
Statue. Plaster cast. The original plaster model, Rome 1816. H. 135,7 cm. Marble version, See A42.

A44 Ganymede with Jupiter's Eagle

Ground floor, room 14.
Statue. Marble version (Thorvaldsen) of the original plaster model executed in 1817 in Rome after a smaller version from 1815. H. 93,3 cm. W. 118,3 cm.

A45 Ganymede with Jupiter's Eagle

First floor, northern corridor.
Statue. Plaster cast. The original plaster model, Rome 1817. H. 88,7 cm. W. 118,3 cm. Marble version,

A46 The Goddess of Hope

Ground floor, room 8.
Statue. Marble version of A47 (Rome 1817) executed in 1859 by H. W. Bissen. H. 160,5 cm.

A47 The Goddess of Hope

First floor, southern corridor.
Statue. Original plaster model. Rome 1817. H. 160,8 cm. Marble version, see A46.

A48 Victory on a Biga

Sketch model. Plaster. Rome 1827. H. 53,8 cm. After Thorvaldsen's death, H. W. Bissen modelled a Victory on a quadriga after this sketch model, a bronze cast of which was erected above the main entrance of the Thorvaldsen Museum .

A49 A Triumphant Muse and Cupid on a Biga

Sketch model. Plaster. Rome 1827. H. 65, 5 cm.

A50 A Triumphant Muse and Cupid on a Biga

Sketch model. Plaster. Rome 1827. H. 71,3 cm.

A51 Jason with the Golden Fleece

Statue. Marble version of A52 (Rome 1802-03) executed in 1846-62 by B. L. Bergslien under the supervision of H. W. Bissen. Formerly in the Thorvaldsen Museum, now in the City Hall of Copenhagen. See A822.

A52 Jason with the Golden Fleece

Ground floor, southern corridor.
Statue. Original plaster model. Rome 1802-03, reworked in the 1830's H. 245,5 cm. Marble versions, see A822 and A51.

A53 Adonis
Ground floor, southern corridor.
Statue. Original plaster model.
Rome 1808. H. 184,5 cm. Marble
version, see A790.

A54 Pollux
Statue. Original plaster model.
Rome 1799. H. 140 cm. Reduced
copy of one of the Horse Tamers on
the Quirinal Piazza (Monte Caval-
lo) in Rome.

A55 Caryatid
Ground floor, western corridor.
Statue. Plaster cast. The original
plaster model, Rome 1813.
H. 203,6 cm. Modelled for a projected monument in Warsaw to
commemorate Napoleon's alliance
with Poland. A marble version of
the statue, placed in the throne
room of Christiansborg Palace in
Copenhagen i 1828, was destroyed
in the palace fire of 1884.

A56 Caryatid
Ground floor, western corridor.
Statue. Plaster cast. The original
plaster model, Rome 1813.
H. 202,5 cm. Companion piece to
A55. See also A735.

A57 The Erythraean Sibyl
Sketch model. Plaster. Inscribed:
"ryth" (from Erythra). Copenhagen,
probably 1820. H. 47,6 cm.

A58 The Cumaean Sibyl
Sketch model. Plaster. Inscribed:
"ma" (from Cumae). Copenhagen,
probably 1820. H. 49 cm.

A59 John the Baptist
Ground floor, northern corridor.
Statue. Plaster cast. H. 239,7 cm.

A59-A70 belong to a group modelled in 1821-22 in Rome for the pediment above the main entrance of
the Church of Our Lady in Copenhagen. A copy in terracotta of the
group was placed there in 1838, but
was later replaced by a marble version, and finally in 1928 by bronze
casts.

A60 Youth
Ground floor, northern corridor.
Statue. Plaster cast. H. 162 cm.
See A59.

A61 Father with his Son
Ground floor, northern corridor.
Statue. Plaster cast. H. 186 cm.
See A59.

A62 Mother with her Son
Ground floor, northern corridor.
Statue. Plaster cast. H. 117,5 cm.
See A59.

A63 Old Scribe
Ground floor, northern corridor.
Statue. Original plaster model.
H. 131 cm. See A59.

A64 Reclining Youth
Ground floor, northern corridor.
Statue. Original plaster model.
H. 92,2 cm. See A59.

A65 Standing Boy
Ground floor, northern corridor.
Statue. Plaster cast. H. 150 cm.
See A59.

A66 Pharisee
Ground floor, northern corridor.
Statue. Original plaster model.
H. 189,5 cm. See A59.

A67 Hunter
Ground floor, northern corridor.
Statue. Plaster cast. H. 188 cm.
See A59.

A68 Two Children
Ground floor, northern corridor.
Statue. Original plaster model.
H. 124,5 cm. See A59.

A69 Mother with her Child
Ground floor, northern corridor.
Statue. Plastercast. H. 132 cm.
See A59.

A70 Reclining Shepherd
Ground floor, northern corridor.
Statue. Original plaster model.
H. 99 cm. See A59.

A71 Roman Warrior
Ground floor, northern corridor.
Statue. Original plaster model.
Rome 1820-21. H. 194 cm. Originally intended for the John the Baptist group A59-70.

A72 Seated Jew
Ground floor, northern corridor.
Statue. Original plaster model.
Rome 1820-21. H. 143 cm. Originally intended for the John the Baptist group A59-70.

A73 John the Baptist
Sketch model for A59. Plaster.
Rome 1820-21. H. 49,7 cm.

A74. Youth
Sketch model for A60. Plaster.
Rome 1820-21. H. 41,3 cm.

A75 Mother with her Son
First sketch model for A62. Plaster.
Rome 1820-21. H. 29,7 cm. The final sketch model for A62 is in the Liebighaus in Frankfurt-on-Main.

A76 Boy with a Dog
Sketch model. Plaster. Rome 1820-21. H. 17,5 cm. Originally intended for the John the Baptist group A59-A70, later replaced by A64.

A77 Mother with her Child
Sketch model for A69. Plaster.
Rome 1820-21. H. 32,3 cm.

A78 Mother with a Sleeping Child
First sketch model for A69. Plaster.
Rome 1820-21. H. 28,5 cm.

A79 Reclining Shepherd
Sketch model for A70. Plaster.
Rome 1820-21. H. 22 cm.

A80 Reclining Shepherd
First sketch model for A70. Plaster.
Rome 1820-21. H. 19,5 cm.

A81 Seated Man
Sketch model for A72. Plaster.
Rome 1820-21. H. 32 cm.

A82 Christ
Ground floor, The Christ Hall.
Statue. Plaster cast of the original plaster model, Rome 1821. H. 345 cm. A marble version was placed in the Church of Our Lady, Copenhagen, in 1839.

A83 Christ
Statue. Preliminary version of A82. Original plaster model. Rome 1821. H. 141,5 cm. Probably modelled by Pietro Tenerani under Thorvaldsen's supervision.

A84 Christ
Sketch model for A82. Plaster.
Rome, probably 1821. H. 60 cm. A preliminary anatomical sketch.

A85 Christ
Sketch model for A82. Plaster.
Rome, probably 1821. H. 55,7 cm.

A86 Peter
Ground floor, The Christ Hall.
Statue. Original plaster model.
Rome 1821. H. 239 cm. A marble
version was placed in the Church of
Our Lady, Copenhagen, in 1839.

A87 Matthew
Ground floor, The Christ Hall.
Statue. Original plaster model.
Rome 1822, H. 239,5 cm.
A marble version was placed in the
Church of Our Lady, Copenhagen,
in 1839.

A88 Matthew
Sketch model for A87. Plaster.
Rome 1821. H. 47,1 cm.

A89 John
Ground floor, The Christ Hall.
Statue. Original plaster model.
Rome 1824, H. 242 cm. A marble
version was placed in the Church of
Our Lady, Copenhagen, in 1839.

A90 John
Sketch model for A89. Plaster.
Rome 1821. H. 49,7 cm.

A91 James the Less
Ground floor, The Christ Hall.
Statue. Original plaster model.
Rome 1824. H. 238 cm. A marble
version was placed in the Church of
Our Lady, Copenhagen, in 1839.

A92 James the Less
Sketch model for A91. Plaster.
Rome 1821-24. H. 51 cm.

A93 Philip
Ground floor, The Christ Hall.
Statue. Original plaster model.

Rome 1824. H. 234,5 cm.
A marble version was placed in the
Church of Our Lady, Copenhagen,
in 1839.

A94 Jude (Thaddaeus)
Statue. Original plaster model
executed in 1823 in Rome by
Giuseppe Pacetti under Thorvaldsen's supervision and reworked in
1827: Later discarded by Thorvaldsen in favour of A105. H. 237 cm.

A95 Andrew
Statue. Original plaster model exe-
cuted in 1823 in Rome by Joseph
Hermann under Thorvaldsen's
supervision. Later discarded by
Thorvaldsen in favour of A108.
H. 238 cm.

A96 Thomas
Ground floor, The Christ Hall.
Statue. Original plaster model.
Rome 1821. H. 240,5 cm.
A marble version was placed in the
Church of Our Lady, Copenhagen,
in 1839.

A97 Thomas
Sketch model for A96. Plaster.
Rome 1821. H. 52,3 cm.

A98 James the Greater
Ground floor, The Christ Hall.
Statue. Original plaster model.
Rome 1821. H. 238 cm. A marble
version was placed in the Church of
Our Lady, Copenhagen, in 1839.

A99 Bartholomew
Ground floor, The Christ Hall.
Statue. Original plaster model.
Rome 1824. H. 244 cm. A marble
version was placed in the Church of
Our Lady, Copenhagen, in 1839.

A100 Bartholomew
Sketch model for A99. Plaster.
Rome 1824. H. 53,2 cm.

A101 Simon Zelotes
Ground floor, The Christ Hall.
Statue. Original plaster model.
Rome 1824. H. 241 cm. A marble
version was placed in the Church of
Our Lady, Copenhagen, in 1839.

A102 Simon Zelotes
Sketch model for A101. Plaster.
Rome, beginning of the 1820's.
H. 50 cm.

A103 Paul
Ground floor, The Christ Hall.
Statue. Original plaster model.
Rome 1821. H. 240,5 cm.
A marble version was placed in the
Church of Our Lady, Copenhagen,
in 1839.

A104 Paul
Sketch model for A103. Plaster.
Rome 1821. H. 50 cm.

A105 Jude (Thaddaeus)
Ground floor, The Christ Hall.
Statue. Original plaster model
executed in 1842 in Rome as a
replacement for A94. H. 236 cm.
A marble version was placed in the
Church of Our Lady, Copenhagen,
before 1848.

A106 Jude (Thaddaeus)
Sketch model for A105. Plaster.
Rome 1841. H. 79,2 cm.

A 107 Jude (Thaddaeus)
First sketch model for A105.
Plaster. Rome 1841. H. 71 cm.

A 108 Andrew
Ground floor, The Christ Hall.
Statue. Original plaster model

executed 1842 in Rome as a
replacement for A95. H. 241 cm.
A marble version was placed in the
Church of Our Lady, Copenhagen,
before 1848.

A109 Andrew
Sketch model for A108. Plaster.
Rome 1841. H. 66,5 cm.

A110 Angel Standing with a Baptismal Font
Ground floor, northern corridor.
Statue. Original plaster model.
Rome 1823. H. 180 cm. Created
for the Church of Our Lady,
Copenhagen, but replaced by the
Kneeling Angel (see A112).
A marble version in the National-
museum, Stockholm.

A111 Angel Standing with a Baptismal Font
Sketch model for A110. Plaster.
Rome between 1820 and 1823.
H. 55,5 cm.

A112 Angel Kneeling with a Baptismal Font
Ground floor, The Christ Hall.
Statue. Plaster cast. The original
plaster model, Rome 1827 or 1828.
H. 141,5 cm. A marble version was
placed in the Church of Our Lady,
Copenhagen, in 1839.
See also A781 .

A 113 Nicolaus Copernicus
Entrance hall.
1473-1543. Astronomer.
Statue. Original plaster model.
Rome 1822. H. 277,2 cm. A bronze
cast, erected in 1830 in Warsaw,
was destroyed during the Second
World War, but restored and reere-
cted in 1950.

A114 Johann Gutenberg

Entrance hall.
C. 1397-1468. The inventor of the art of printing.
Statue. Original plaster model executed in 1833-34 in Rome by H. W. Bissen under Thorvaldsen's direction and supervision. H. 348,5 cm. A bronze cast erected 1837 in Mainz.

A115 The Invention of the Movable Type

Entrance hall.
Relief for the base of the Gutenberg monument (see A114).
Original plaster model executed in 1833-34 in Rome by H. W. Bissen under Thorvaldsen's direction and supervision. H. 90,5 cm. W. 118,5 cm. A bronze cast was placed on the monument in Mainz in 1837.

A116 The Invention of the Printing Press

Entrance hall.
Relief for the base of the Gutenberg monument (see A114).
Original plaster model executed in 1833-34 in Rome by H. W. Bissen under Thorvaldsen's direction and supervision. H. 91 cm. W. 118,5 cm. A bronze cast was placed on the monument in Mainz in 1837.

A117 Johann Gutenberg

C. 1397-1468. The inventor of the art of printing.
Sketch model for A114. Plaster. Modelled in Rome in 1833 by H. W. Bissen under Thorvaldsen's direction. H. 54 cm.

A118 The Invention of the Printing Press

First floor, room 33.
Sketch model for A116. Rome probably 1833. H. 40 cm. W. 51,5 cm.

A119 Dying Lion Protecting the Royal Arms of France (The Lucerne Lion)

Ground floor, western corridor.
Statue. Plaster cast. The original plaster model, Rome 1819. H. 84 cm. W. 161 cm. Cut in colossal size by Lucas Ahorn in the side of a cliff at Lucerne in memory of the Swiss Guards who fell in Paris during the Terror in 1792; completed in 1821.

A120 Monument to Karl Philipp von Schwarzenberg

1771-1820. Austrian prince and general, Duke of Krumau.
Sketch model for unexecuted monument. Plaster. Rome 1821. H. 97 cm.

A121 Recumbent Lion

Ground floor, room 13.
Statue. Marble version (Thorvaldsen) of A122 (Rome 1825). H. 88 cm. Probably intended for the projected monument to Karl Philipp von Schwarzenberg (see A120).

A122 Recumbent Lion

Ground floor, western corridor.
Statue. Original plaster model. Rome 1825. H. 87,5 cm. Marble version, see A121.

A123 Józef Poniatowski
Entrance hall.
1763-1813. Polish prince and general.
Equestrian statue. Original plaster model. Rome 1826-27. H. 463 cm. The statue was commissioned in 1817 and the final contract signed in 1820. Cast in bronze, it was to have been erected in Warsaw in 1832. This was forbidden by Emperor Nicholas I; he presented it to General Paskewitch, who erected it on his estate Gomel in the province of Mogilev in Russia. In 1921 it was restored to Warsaw, where it was erected in the Saxon Square in 1923. In 1944 it was blown up by the Nazi occupational forces before they abandoned the city. A new bronze statue, made after the original plaster model, was presented to the city of Warsaw by the Danish Government and the Corporation of Copenhagen, and unveiled in 1952.

A124 Józef Poniatowski
Ground floor, room 12.
1763-1813. Polish prince and general .
Equestrian statue. Partly an original plaster model. Rome 1826. Preliminary version of A123. H. 255 cm.

A125 Horse
Ground floor, western corridor.
Statue. Partly an original plaster model executed 1822-23 in Rome as a preliminary work for A123. H. 208,2 cm.

A126 Jozef Poniatowski
First floor, room 30.
1763-1813. Polish prince and general .
Sketch model for A123. Plaster. Rome 1822. H. 82,5 cm.

A127 Maximilian I
1573-1651. Elector of Bavaria. Sketch model for A128. Plaster. Rome 1830-32. H. 80 cm.

A128 & A762 Maximilian I
Entrance hall.
1573-1651. Elector of Bavaria. Equestrian statue. The horse (A128) an original plaster model, Maximilian I (A762) a plastercast, acquired in 1855. Rome 1833-35. H. 522,5 cm. A bronze cast erected in 1839 in Munich.

A129 Horse
Ground floor, western corridor.
Statue. Partly an original plaster model executed in 1832-33 in Rome as a preliminary work for A128. H. 199 cm.

A130 Georg Gordon, Lord Byron
Ground floor, room 13.
1788-1824. English poet. Statue. Original plaster model. Rome 1831. H. 174 cm. A first model for the marble version in Trinity College, Cambridge.

A131 The Genius of Poetry
Ground floor, room 13.
Relief for the base of Lord Byron's monument A130. Marble version of A134 (Rome 1831).
H. 80,2 cm. W. 59 cm.

A132 Georg Gordon, Lord Byron
First floor, southern corridor.
1788-1824. English poet. Statue. Plaster cast, the head from the bust A257 (Rome 1817), the rest from the original plaster model A130 (Rome 1831). H. 173,5 cm. A marble version in Trinity College, Cambridge.

A133 George Gordon, Lord Byron
1788-1824. English poet.
Sketch model for A130. Plaster.
Rome 1830. H. 51,5 cm.

A134 The Genius of Poetry
First floor, southern corridor.
Relief.
Original plaster model. Rome 1831.
H. 79 cm. W. 60,5 cm. Marble
version, see A131.

A135 The Apotheosis of Schiller
Relief for the base of the Schiller
monument (see A770).
Original plaster model executed in
1837 in Rome by Wilh. Matthiä
after a sketch by Thorvaldsen from
1835. H. 62 cm. W. 127,5 cm.
A bronze cast placed 1839 on the
monument in Stuttgart.

A136 The Genius of Poetry
Entrance hall.
Relief for the base of the Schiller
monument (see A770).
Original plaster model executed in
1837 in Rome by Wilh. Matthiä
after a sketch by Thorvaldsen from
1835. See also A526. H. 84,5 cm.
W. 88,3 cm. A bronze cast placed
1839 on the monument in
Stuttgart.

A137 The Goddess of Victory
Relief for the base of the Schiller
monument (see A770).
Original plaster model executed in
1837 in Rome by Wilh. Matthiä
after a sketch by Thorvaldsen from
1835. H. 84,5 cm. W. 88,5 cm.
A bronze cast placed 1839 on the
monument in Stuttgart.

A138 Friedrich Schiller
1759-1805. German poet.
Sketch model for A770. Plaster cast.
Rome 1835. H. 83,5 cm.

A139 Johann Wolfgang Goethe
1749-1832. German poet.
Sketch model for a projected
monument in Frankfurt-on-Main
of the poet seated. Plaster cast.
Copenhagen, probably 1839.
H. 45,5 cm.

A140 Johann Wolfgang Goethe
1749-1832. German poet.
Sketch model for a projected monument in Frankfurt of the poet standing. Plaster. Copenhagen, probably 1840. H. 69,5 cm.

A141 Frederik VI
1768-1839. King of Denmark
1808.
Sketch model for a projected
monument. Plaster. Copenhagen,
December 1839. H. 45 cm.

A142 Pius VII
Entrance hall.
1742-1823. Gregorio Barnaba
Chiaramonti. Pope 1800.
Statue. Original plaster model.
Rome 1824-25. H. 295,3 cm.
A marble version was placed on the
monument to Pius VII in Saint
Peter's in Rome, unveiled in 1831.

A143 Heavenly Wisdom
Entrance hall.
Statue. Original plaster model.
Rome 1825. H. 290,5 cm.
A marble version was placed on the
monument to Pius VII in Saint
Peter's in Rome, uneveiled 1831.

A144 Divine Power
Entrance hall.
Statue. Original plaster model.
Rome 1825. H. 304,5 cm.
A marble version was placed on the monument to Pius VII in Saint Peter's in Rome, unveiled 1831.

A145 The Coat of Arms of Pius VII Held by Two Angels
Entrance hall.
Relief. Original plaster model.
Rome c. 1824-30. H. 67,5 cm.
W. 207,5 cm. A marble version was placed on the monument to Pius VII in Saint Peter's in Rome, unveiled in 1831.

A146 Angel
Ground floor, northern corridor.
Statue. Original plaster model.
Rome 1830. H. 141,5 cm.
A marble version was placed on the monument to Pius VII in Saint Peter's in Rome, unveiled in 1831.

A147 Angel
Ground floor, northern corridor.
Statue. Original plaster model.
Rome 1830. H. 147,5 cm.
A marble version was placed on the monument to Pius VII in Saint Peter's in Rome, unveiled in 1831.

A148 Monument to Pope Pius VII
Sketch model for A142-A145.
Plaster. Rome 1824. H. 107 cm.

A149 Pius VII
1742-1823. Gregorio Barnaba Chiaramonti. Pope 1800.
Sketch model for A142. Plaster.
Rome 1824. H. 44 cm.

A150 Conradin
Ground floor, room 21.
1252-1268. The last of the Hohenstaufens.
Statue. Original plaster model.
Rome 1836. H. 212,3 cm. A marble version was placed on Conradin's tomb in the church of Santa Maria del Carmine, Naples, in 1847.

A151 Conradin
1252-1268. The last of the Hohenstaufens .
Sketch model for A150. Plaster.
Rome 1833. H. 53 cm.

A152 Christian IV
Ground floor, room 21.
1577-1648. King of Denmark 1588.
Statue. Original plaster model.
Copenhagen 1840. H. 212,3 cm.
A bronze cast, executed by .
B. Dalhoff, erected 1845 in the Chapel of Christian IV in the Cathedral of Roskilde.

A153 Three Genii
First floor, room 33.
The motto of Christian IV: *Regna firmat pietas.*
Relief. Original plaster model.
Inscribed: "Nysø 25 November 1842". H. 56 cm. W. 78 cm.
Originally intended for the monument to Christian IV in the Cathedral of Roskilde. See A152.

A155 Wlodzimierz Potocki
Ground floor, southern corridor.
1789-1812. Polish count and general.
Statue. Original plaster model.
Rome 1821. H. 215,2 cm. A marble version was placed on the Count's tomb in the Wawel Cathedral in Cracow in 1832 (see also A626 and A627). Another marble version, A794, was executed for the Museum.

A156 Eugène de Beauharnais
Entrance hall.
1781-1824. Duke of Leuchtenberg, Napoleon I's stepson and Viceroy of Italy.
Statue. Original plaster model. Rome 1827. H. 275 cm. A marble version was placed on the Duke's tomb in the Church of Saint Michael, Munich, in 1830.

A157 The Genii of Life and Death
Sketch model. Plaster. Rome, probably 1825. H. 41,4 cm. Pietro Tenerani modelled a group after this sketch model in 1827, a marble version of which was placed on the sepulchral monument to the Duke of Leuchtenberg in 1830. See A156.

A158 The Genii of Life and Death beside a Meta
Sketch model. Plaster. Rome, probably between 1815 and 1819. H. 82, 5 cm.

A159 Kneeling Angel
Sketch model for a statue, probably executed for the tomb of a daughter of Daniel Jacobi in Lübeck. Plaster. Nysø 1839. H. 43,7 cm.

A160 Martin Luther
1483-1546. German reformer.
Sketch model for a projected statue for the vestibule of the Church of Our Lady, Copenhagen. Plaster. Rome, probably 1838. H. 68 cm.

A161 Philipp Melanchthon
1497-1560. German reformer.
Sketch model for a projected statue for the vestibule of the Church of Our Lady, Copenhagen. Plaster. Rome, probably 1838. H. 67 cm.

A162 Bertel Thorvaldsen Leaning on the Statue of Hope
Ground floor, southern corridor.
1770-1844. Self-portrait.
Statue. Plaster cast. The original plaster model, Nysø 1839. H. 198 cm. Marble version, see A771. For the Goddess of Hope, see A46.

A163 Bertel Thorvaldsen
1770-1844. Self-portrait.
Sketch model for A162. Plaster cast. Nysø 1839. H. 65 cm.

A164 Caroline Amalie
Ground floor, room 21.
1796-1881. Princess, later Queen of Denmark, married to Christian Frederik (Christian VIII).
Statue. Original plaster model. Rome 1827. H. 175 cm.

A166 Yelizaveta Alexeyevna Osterman-Tolstoy
Ground floor, room 11.
1779-1835. Russian countess.
Statue. Marble version of A167 (Rome 1815) executed 1863 by C. C. Olsen under the supervision of H. W. Bissen. H. 138 cm.

A167 Yelizaveta Alexeyevna Osterman-Tolstoy
First floor, southern corridor.
1779-1835. Russian countess.
Statue. Original plaster model. Rome 1815. H. 136 cm. Marble version, see A166.

A168 Seated Lady
Sketch model. Plaster. Rome, probably between 1815 and 1819. H. 44,3 cm.

A169 Seated Lady
Sketch model. Plaster. Rome, probably between 1815 and 1819. H. 42 cm.

A170 Seated Lady with a Boy
Sketch model. Plaster. Rome, probably between 1815 and 1819. H. 42

A171 Maria Fyodorovna Baryatinskaya
Ground floor, room 11.
1793-1858. Nee Keller, married to the Russian Prince Ivan Ivanovitch Baryatinsky. Statue. Marble version (Thorvaldsen) of A172 (Rome 1818), executed c. 1819-25. H. 181 cm.

A172 Maria Fyodorovna Baryatinskaya
First floor, southern corridor.
1793-1858. Nee Keller, married to the Russian Prince Ivan Ivanovitch Baryatinsky. Statue. Original plaster model. Rome 1818. H. 180 cm. Marble version, see A171.

A173 Georgiana Elizabeth Russell
First floor, southern corridor.
C. 1810-1867. Daughter of John Russell, Duke of Bedford. Statue. Plaster cast. The original plaster model, Rome 1815. H. 100,3 cm. Marble version, see A773.

A174 Jeanina Emilie Stampe as Psyche
First floor, northern corridor.
1833-1861. Daughter of Baron Henrik Stampe and Baroness Christine Stampe.

Statue. Original plaster model. Inscribed: "Nysøe d:l2 novb. 1840". H. 105 cm.

A175 Pietro Alberto Paulsen as a Hunter Boy
1834-1921. Son of Fritz Paulsen and Elisa Paulsen, nee Thorvaldsen, Thorvaldsen's grandson. Sketch model. Plaster. Nysø 1843. H. 42,8 cm.

A176 Shepherd Boy
See A895.

A177 Shepherd Boy
First floor, northern corridor.
Statue. Original plaster model. Rome 1817. H. 148,5 cm. Marble version, see A895.

A178 Dancing Girl
First floor, southern corridor.
Statue. Original plaster model. Rome 1817. H. 175,5 cm.

A179 Dancing Girl
First floor, southern corridor.
Statue. An adaptation of A178. Plaster cast. Rome, between 1817 and 1822. H. 174,5 cm.

A180 Young Dancing Girl
First floor, room 26.
Statue. Marble version of A181 (Rome 1837) begun in Thorvaldsen's Roman studio and completed after his death. H. 151 cm.

A181 Young Dancing Girl
First floor, northern corridor.
Statue. Original plaster model. Rome 1837. H. 146,5 cm. Marble version, see A180.

A182 Young Dancing Girl
Sketch model for A181. Plaster.
Rome, probably 1837. H. 60 cm.

A184 Flower Girl
Sketch model. Plaster. H. 70 cm.

A185 Youth with a Dog
Sketch model. Plaster. H. 60 cm.

A186 Apollinaris of Ravenna
Ground floor, southern corridor.
Died 75 A. D. (?) First bishop of
Ravenna and martyr.
Bust. Original plaster model. Rome
1821. H. 97,5 cm.

A 187 Leonardo Pisano, Fibonacci
Ground floor, southern corridor.
C. 1170-c. 1240. Italian mathematician.
Bust. Marble version (Thorvaldsen)
of the original plaster model A722
executed in Rome between 1834
and 1838 for the Protomoteca
Capitolina, but never placed. Inscribed: "Leonardo Pisano detto
Fibonacci principe de' Matematici
visse nel secolo XII"; on the sides:
"Monsignor Girolamo Galanti
pose", and "Alberto Thorvaldsen
scolpi". H. 72,7 cm.

A188 Martin Luther
1483-1546. German reformer.
Unfinished bust. Original plaster
model. Copenhagen 1844. H. 55,4
cm, Thorvaldsen's last work.

A189 Maximilian I
Ground floor, southern corridor.
1573-1651. Elector of Bavaria.
Bust. Preliminary work for A762
(see A128). Original plaster model.
Rome 1831. H. 66,5 cm.

A190 Ludvig Holberg
1684-1754. Danish playwright,
historian, and philosopher.
Bust. Plaster cast. The original
plaster model A876, Nysø and
Copenhagen 1839. H. 55,2 cm.

A191 Frederik VI
Ground floor, room 21.
1768-1839. King of Denmark from
1808.
Bust. Plaster cast. The original plaster model, Copenhagen 1819-20.
H. 71,2 cm. Marble version, see
A859.

A192 Marie Sophie Frederikke
Ground floor, room 21.
1767-1852. Queen of Denmark,
married to Frederik VI.
Bust. Original plaster model.
Copenhagen 1819-20. H. 75 cm.
Marble version, see A860.

A193 Caroline
Ground floor, room 21.
1793-1881. Danish princess,
daughter of Frederik VI.
Bust. Original plaster model.
Copenhagen 1819-20. H. 71,8 cm.
Marble version, see A857.

A194 Vilhelmine Marie
First floor, room 22.
1808-1891. Danish princess,
daughter of Frederik VI.
Bust. Original plaster model.
Copenhagen 1819-20. H. 46,4 cm.

A195 Vilhelmine Marie
Ground floor, room 18.
1808-1891. Danish princess,
daughter of Frederik VI.
Bust. Marble version (Thorvaldsen)
of A196 (Rome 1828). H. 70,3 cm.

A196 Vilhelmine Marie
Ground floor, room 21.
1808-1891. Danish princess,
daughter of Frederik VI.
Bust. Original plaster model. Rome
1828. H. 69,5 cm. Marble version,
see A195.

A197 Christian Frederik
1786-1848. Danish prince, from
1839 King Christian VIII of Denmark. Bust. Plaster cast. The original plaster model A753, Rome
1821. H. 58,8 cm.

A198 Caroline Amalie
1796-1881. Princess, later Queen of
Denmark, married to Christian Frederik (Christian VIII).
Bust. Plaster cast. The original plaster model A716, Rome 1820-21.
H. 53,3 cm. See also A754.

A199 Frederik Carl Christian
Ground floor, room 20.
1808-1863. Danish prince, from
1848 King Frederik VII of
Denmark.
Bust. Original plaster model.
Copenhagen 1820. H. 43,4 cm.
A marble version belongs to Rosen-
borg Castle, see Dep. 33.

A200 Frederik Carl Christian
Ground floor, room 20.
1808-1863. Danish prince, from
1848 King Frederik VII of Denmark.
Bust. Marble version (Thorvaldsen)
of the original plaster model executed 1828 in Rome. H. 67,6 cm.

A201 Friedrich Wilhelm Carl Ludwig
Ground floor, room 21.
1786-1834. Prince of Hessen-
Philippsthal-Barchfeld.
Bust. Plaster cast. The original plas-
ter model, Rome 1822. H. 61,6 cm.

A202 Juliane Sophie
Ground floor, room 21.
1788-1850. Danish princess,
daughter of Heir-Presumptive
Prince Frederik, married to Prince
Friedrich Wilhelm of Hessen-
Philippsthal-Barchfeld.
Bust. Plaster cast. The original plas-
ter model, Rome 1822. H. 60,6 cm.

A203 Christian Carl Friedrich August
First floor, room 12.
1798-1869. Duke of Augustenborg.
Bust. Marble version (Thorvaldsen)
of A204 (Rome 1819). H. 57 cm.

A204 Christian Carl Friedrich August
1798-1869. Duke of Augustenborg.
Bust. Original plaster model. Rome
1819. H. 55 cm. Marble version,
see A203.

A205 Friedrich August Emil
Ground floor, room 12.
1800-1865. Prince of Augustenborg.
Bust. Marble version (Thorvaldsen)
of A206 (Rome 1819). H. 70,5 cm.

A206 Friedrich August Emil
1800-1865. Prince of Augustenborg.
Bust. Original plaster model. Rome
1819. H. 69 cm. Marble version,
see A205.

A207 Andreas Peter Bernstorff
Ground floor, room 12.
1735-1797. Danish statesman and count.
Bust. Marble version (Thorvaldsen) of the original plaster model executed in 1804 in Rome. H. 47,9 cm. A colossal version, see A209.

A208 Andreas Peter Bernstorff
1735-1797. Danish statesman and count.
Bust. Reworked version of A856. Original plaster model. Rome 1797. H. 51,5 cm.

A209 Andreas Peter Bernstorff
1735-1797. Danish statesman and count.
Bust. Original plaster model. Rome 1804. H. 84,8 cm. Reduced marble version, see A207.

A210 Henrik Hielmstierne
Ground floor, room 13.
1715-1780. Danish Titular Privy Councillor and art collector.
Bust, modelled after a plaster cast of a bust by Hartman Beeken and a drawing after a painting by Jens Juel. Original plaster model. Rome, probably 1812. H. 53,7 cm.

A211 Conrad Rantzau-Breitenburg
Ground floor, northern corridor.
1773-1845. Danish statesman and count.
Bust. Original plaster model. Rome 1805. H. 74,3 cm.

A212 Adam Gottlob Detlef Moltke of Nütschau
Ground floor, entrance hall.
1765-1843. Danish count and poet.
Bust. Original plaster model. Rome 1803-04. H. 81,4 cm.

A213 Hans Holsten
First floor, northern corridor.
1758-1849. Danish baron and admiral.
Bust. Original plaster model. Inscribed: "Den 17. Novemb. 1840". Nysø. H. 56 cm.

A214 Conrad Danneskiold-Samsøe
First floor, room 24.
1774-1823. Danish count and Lord Lieutenant.
Bust. Original plaster model. Nordfeld 1820. H. 49,3 cm.

A215 Henriette Danneskiold-Samsøe
First floor, western corridor.
1776-1843. Née Kaas, married to Conrad Danneskiold-Samsøe.
Bust. Original plaster model. Inscribed: "A. Thorvaldsen Nysøe d. 6. December 1839". H. 48,7 cm.

A216 Louise Danneskiold-Samsøe
First floor, room 24.
1796-1867. Daughter of Conrad Danneskiold-Samsøe, 1820, married to Duke Christian of Augustenborg.
Bust. Original plaster model. Gisselfeld 1820. H. 49,9 cm.

A217 Christine Stampe
First floor, western corridor.
1797-1868. Danish baroness, nee
Dalgas, married to Baron Henrik
Stampe.
Bust. Plaster cast. Inscribed: "Roma
Maggio 1842". H. 57,4 cm.

A218 Ida Brun
First floor, northern corridor.
1792-1857. Daughter of Constantin and Friederike Brun. Married
Count Louis Philippe Bombelles,
Austrian diplomat.
Bust. Original plaster model. Rome
1809. H. 57 cm. Marble version,
see A810.

A219 Herman Schubart
Entrance hall.
1756-1832. Danish baron and
diplomat in Italy (Leghorn).
Bust. Marble version (Thorvaldsen)
of A718 (Montenero 1804).
H. 70,4 cm. See also A812.

A220 Jacoba Elisabeth Schubart
Entrance hall.
1765-1814. Née de Wieling, married to Baron Herman Schubart.
Bust. Marble version (Thorvaldsen)
of A719 (Montenero 1804).
H. 69,6 cm. See also A813.

A221 Frederik Siegfried Vogt
Ground floor, room 12.
1777-1855. Danish diplomat and
charge d'affaires in Naples.
Bust. Marble version (Thorvaldsen)
of A222 (Rome 1837). H. 62,3 cm.

A222 Frederik Siegfried Vogt
First floor, northern corridor.
1777-1855. Danish diplomat and
charge d'affaires in Naples.

Bust. Original plaster model. Rome
1837. H. 60,5 cm. Marble version,
see A221.

A223 Bertel Thorvaldsen
Ground floor, southern corridor.
1770-1844. Self-portrait.
Bust. Plaster cast of the marble
version (Thorvaldsen) in the Royal
Academy of Fine Arts in Copenhagen. The original plaster model
executed in 1810 in Rome.
H. 73,5 cm.

A224 Christoffer Wilhelm Eckersberg
1783-1853. Danish painter.
Bust. Original plaster model. Inscribed: "Eckersberg Roma li 12
Maggio 1816". H. 51 cm. Marble
version, see A788.

A225 Tyge Rothe
1731-1795. Danish philosopher.
Bust. Marble version (Thorvaldsen)
of the original plaster model executed in 1797 in Rome. Inscribed:
"Tyge Rothe". H. 45,5 cm.

A226 Adam Oehlenschläger
First floor, northern corridor.
1779-1850. Danish poet.
Bust. Original plaster model.
Inscribed: "Nysøe den 29. Set.
1839". H.54,1 cm.

A227 Caspar Bartholin
First floor, southern corridor.
1782-1805. Danish Bachelor of
Laws.
Bust. Original plaster model.Rome,
probably 1818-19. H. 58,1 cm.

A228 Sophie Dorothea Høyer
First floor, room 26.
C. 1743-1808. Née Heldvad, married to the Lutheran pastor Jens Offesen Høyer, and mother of the painter C. F. Høyer.
Bust. Original plaster model. Rome 1809. H. 47,8 cm. Marble version, see A763.

A229 Johan Christian Dahl
First floor, room 12.
1788-1857. Norwegian painter.
Bust. Original plaster model. Rome 1821. H. 51,8 cm.

A230 Jørgen von Cappelen Knudtzon
First floor, northern corridor.
1784-1854. Norwegian merchant.
Bust. Original plaster model. Rome 1816. H. 57,7 cm.

A231 Hans Carl Knudtzon
First floor, northern corridor.
1794-1821. Norwegian merchant.
Bust. Original plaster model. Rome 1816. H. 53,5 cm.

A232 Ludwig
First floor, room 20.
1786-1868. Crown Prince, later King Ludwig I of Bavaria 1825-48.
Bust. Marble version (Thorvaldsen) of A233 (Rome 1818). H. 67,9 cm.

A233 Ludwig
Ground floor, southern corridor.
1786-1868. Crown Prince, later King Ludwig I of Bavaria 1825-48.
Bust. Original plaster model. Rome 1818. H. 68 cm. Marble version, see A232.

A234 Clemens Metternich
First floor, room 12.
1773-1859. Austrian statesman, count, later prince.
Bust. Marble version (Thorvaldsen) of A235 (Rome 1819). H. 61 cm.

A235 Clemens Metternich
First floor, room 17.
1773-1859. Austrian statesman, count, later prince.
Bust. Original plaster model. Rome 1819. H. 63,2 cm. Marble version, see A234.

A236 Karl Philipp von Schwarzenberg
First floor, room 12.
1771-1820. Austrian prince and general, Duke of Krumau.
Bust. Original plaster model. Rome 1821. H. 54 cm.

A237 Wilhelm von Humboldt
First floor, room 9.
1767-1835. German baron, philologist, diplomat, and statesman.
Bust. Original plaster model. Rome 1808. H. 53,5 cm.

A238 Alexandrine von Dietrichstein
First floor, western corridor.
1775-1847. Née Countess Sjuvalov, married to the Austrian Prince Franz Josef Johann von Dietrichstein.
Bust. Original plaster model. Rome c. 1810. H. 55,5 cm.

A239 Giovanna Nugent
First floor, room 11.
1795-1854. Née Riario-Sforza,
married to the Irish Count Laval
Nugent-Westmeath.
Bust. Original plaster model.
Naples, probably 1818.
H. 56,1 cm.

A240 Christian August Tiedge
1752-1841. German poet.
Bust. Original plaster model. Rome
c. 1805-06. H. 65 cm.

A241 Henri François Brandt
First floor, room 12.
1789-1845. Swiss medal engraver.
Bust. Original plaster model. Rome,
probably 1817. H. 55,2 cm.

A242 Conrad Hinrich Donner
First floor, room 12.
1774-1854. Danish merchant in
Altona.
Bust. Original plaster model.
Copenhagen 1840. H. 57,1 cm.

A243 Bernhard von Eichthal
First floor, northern corridor.
1784-1830.
Bust. Original plaster model.
Rome ç. 1830-31. H. 53,6 cm.

A244 Mrs. von Krause
First floor, room 31.
Probably the wife of Jacob von
Krause, Austrian Consul General
in St. Petersburg.
Bust. Original plaster model. Rome
1819. H. 55,2 cm.

A245 Karoline von Rehfues
Ground floor, room 3.
1799-1892. Née von Meusebach,
married to the German writer
Philipp Joseph von Rehfues.

Bust. Original plaster model. Rome
1827. H. 53,2 cm. Marble version,
see A861.

A246 Alexander I
1777-1825. Czar of Russia 1801.
Bust. Plaster cast. The original
plaster model A715, Warsaw 1820.
H. 67,6 cm.

A247 Helen of Russia
Ground floor, northern corridor.
1807-1873. Née Princess of Würt-
temberg, married to Mikhail Pavlo-
vitch, Grand Duke of Russia.
Bust. Original plaster model. Rome
1829. H. 73 cm.

A248 Maria Alekseyevna Narishkin
Ground floor, room 15.
1762-1822. Née Senyavina, married to Alexander Lvovitch Narish-
kin, Grand Chamberlain at the
Russian Court.
Bust. Original plaster model. Rome
c. 1815-16. H. 66 cm.

A249 Jozef Poniatowski
First floor, southern corridor.
1763-1813. Polish prince and
general.
Bust. Preliminary work for A123.
Original plaster model. Rome 1819.
H. 59,7 cm.

A250 Maria Fyodorovna Baryatinskaya
First floor, southern corridor.
1793-1858. Née Keller, married to
the Russian Prince Ivan Ivanovitch
Baryatinsky.
Bust. Preliminary work for A171.
Original plaster modcl. Rome 1818.
H. 57, 5 cm.

A251 Anna Potocka?
First floor, western corridor.
1776-1867. Née Tyszkiewicz, married to the Polish Count Aleksander Potocki.
Bust. Original plaster model. Rome c. 1814-16 or 1820? H. 57,3 cm.

A252 Napoleon I
1769-1821. Emperor of France 1804-14.
Bust. Plaster cast. The original plaster model A909, Rome c. 1830. H. 100 cm. Marble versions, see A732 and A867.

A253 Horace Vernet
Entrance hall.
1789-1863. French painter.
Bust. Marble version in colossal size of A254 (Rome 1832), begun in 1834 in Rome, and completed in 1856 in Copenhagen under the supervision of H. W. Bissen. H. 110,5 cm.

A254 Horace Vernet
Ground floor, room 1.
1789-1863. French painter.
Bust. Original plaster model. Rome 1832. H. 48,9 cm. Marble version, see A253.

A255 Sir Walter Scott
Ground floor, southern corridor.
1771-1832. Scottish author.
Bust. Plaster cast. The original plaster model, Rome c. 1832. H. 73,6

A256 George Gordon, Lord Byron
Ground floor, room 13.
1788-1824. English poet.
Bust. Marble version of A257 (Rome 1817). H. 65,3 cm.

A257 George Gordon, Lord Byron
Ground floor, southern corridor.
1788-1824. English poet.
Bust. Original plaster model. Rome 1817. H. 66,9 cm. Marble version, see A256. See also A132.

A258 Thomas Maitland
Entrance hall.
1759-1824. Lord High Commissioner of the Ionian Islands.
Bust. Modelled after a plaster cast of a bust, probably by Paolo Prossalendi. Original plaster model. Rome 1818. H. 130,4 cm. In 1820 a bronze cast of the bust and of the relief A600 were placed on a monument on the Island of Zakynthos. The bust in bronze was lost during the Second World War.

A259 George Granville Leveson, Lord Gower
Ground floor, room 17.
1786-1861. Later Duke of Sutherland.
Bust. Original plaster model. Rome 1817. H. 57,1 cm.

A260 Edward Pellew
Ground floor, room 13.
1757-1833. English baron, later First Viscount Exmouth. Admiral.
Bust. Original plaster model. Rome 1814. H. 51,3 cm.

A261 William Cavendish, Lord Bentinck
1774-1839. 1803-07 Governor of Madras, later Envoy Extraordinary to the Sicilian Court.
Bust. Original plaster model. Rome 1815 or 1816. H. 49,9 cm.

A262 Alexander Baillie
First floor, northern corridor.
1777-1855. Scottish, of the Baillies
of Dochfour.
Bust. Original plaster model. Rome
1816. H. 59 cm.

A263 Edward Divett
Ground floor, room 12.
C. 1777-1819. Squire of Bystock,
Devon.
Bust. Original plaster model. Rome
1817. H. 64,5 cm.

A264 Louisa Hope
First floor, western corridor.
C. 1786-1851. Née de la Poer
Beresford, married to Thomas
Hope.
Bust. Original plaster model. Rome
1817. H. 58,3 cm. Marble version,
see A824.

A265 Henry Thomas Hope
1808-1862. Son of Thomas and
Louisa Hope.
Bust. Original plaster model. Rome
c. 1822-23. H. 47,3 cm. Marble
version, see A825.

A266 Henry Thomas Hope?
1808-1862. Son of Thomas and
Louisa Hope.
Bust. Plaster cast. The original plas-
ter model. Rome c. 1817.
H. 46,4 cm.

A267 Mary Ann Montagu
Ground floor, southern corridor.
1781-1862. Daughter of Armar
Corry, Earl of Balmore. Married to
George John Montagu, Earl of
Sandwich.
Bust. Original plaster model. Rome
1816. H. 69,9 cm.

A268 Eliza, Lady Glenorchy
Ground floor, southern corridor.
1803-1861. Nee Baillie, married to
John Campbell, Lord Glenorchy,
later Marquis of Breadalbane.
Bust. Original plaster model.
Rome c. 1829. H. 72 cm.

A269 Julia Potocka
First floor, western corridor.
C. 1760-1794. Nee Lubomirska,
married to the Polish Count Jan
Potocki.
Bust. Original plaster model. Rom
c. 1832-33. H. 67,2 cm.

A270 Pius VII
Ground floor, western corridor.
1742-1823. Gregorio Barnaba
Chiaramonti. Pope from 1800.
Bust. Preliminary work for A142.
Original plaster model. Rome 1824.
H. 67,3 cm.

A271 Ercole Consalvi
Ground floor, western corridor.
1757-1824. Italian cardinal.
Bust. Original plaster model. Rome
1824. H. 73,9 cm. A marble version was placed on Consalvi's tomb
in the Pantheon, Rome, in 1824.

A272 Giovanni-Battista Sommariva
Ground floor, room 12.
C. 1750-1826. Italian count, politi-
cian, and art collector.
Bust. Marble version of A273
(Rome 1817 or 1818). H. 51,5 cm.
See also A741.

A273. Giovanni-Battista Sommariva
Ground floor, room 7.
C. 1750-1826. Italian count, politician, and art collector.
Bust. Original plaster model. Rome 1817 or 1818. H. 49 cm. Marble version, see A272 and A741.

A274 Giovanni-Battista Sommariva
First floor, northern corridor.
C. 1750-1826. Italian count, politician, and art collector.
Bust. Original plaster model. Rome c. 1821. H. 54,6 cm.

A275 Georg Wilhelm Wilding
1790-1841. Married to Donna Catharina di Branciforte, became the Principe di Butera in 1814 after the death of his father-in-law.
Bust. Original plaster model. Rome 1815. H. 69,6 cm. Marble version, see A890.

A276 Catharina di Branciforte
1768-1824. Née Branciforte e Pignatelli, daughter of the Principe di Butera. Married 1812 to Georg Wilhelm Wilding. 1814 Principessa di Butera.
Bust. Original plaster model. Rome 1815. H. 70,5 cm. Marble version, see A891.

A277 Giovanni Raimondo Torlonia
First floor, southern corridor.
1754-1829. Duke of Bracciano, Roman banker.
Bust. Plaster cast. The original plaster model, Rome 1829. H. 54,2 cm.

A278 Marianna Florenzi
1802-1870. Née Baccinetti, married to Marchese Ettore Florenzi.
Bust. Original plaster model. Rome 1828. H. 71,9 cm. Modelled at the order of King Ludwig I of Bavaria as a companion piece to his own bust A233. Marble version, see A727.

A279 Vittoria Caldoni
1807-? Italian model from Albano.
Bust. Original plaster model. Rome 1821. H. 53,2 cm. Marble version, see A886.

A280 Ghazi 'L-Din Haidar
Ground floor, southern corridor.
Padishah of Oudh, King of Oudh 1819-27.
Bust. Original plaster model. Rome 1824. H. 82 cm. Marble version, see A887 .

A281 Vincenzo Camuccini
Ground floor, room 20.
1771-1844. Italian painter.
Bust. Marble version (Thorvaldsen) of A282 (Rome 1810). H. 56,2 cm.

A282 Vincenzo Camuccini
1771-1844. Italian painter.
Bust. Original plaster model. Rome 1810. H. 57,7 cm. Marble version, see A281.

A283 John Wyllie
Ground floor, northern corridor.
?-1848. Scottish surgeon.
Bust. Original plaster model. Rome 1831. H. 73,5 cm.

A284 Unknown Man
Bust. Original plaster model. Rome, probably 1830's. H. 50,5 cm.

A285 Wriothesley Russell?
Ground floor, room 1.
1804-1886. Lord Russell. Son of
John Russell, sixth Duke of
Bedford.
Bust. Original plaster model. Rome
c. 1828. H. 50,9 cm.

A286 Charles James Patrick Mahon?
First floor, southern corridor.
1800-1891. Irish politician.
Bust. Original plaster model.
Rome c. 1832. H. 61,4 cm.

A287 Unknown Man
Ground floor, room 7.
Bust. Original plaster model. Rome,
probably 1830's. H. 50,3 cm.

A288 Yuri Aleksandrovitch Golovkin
Ground floor, room 9.
1762-1846. Russian diplomat,
Count.
Bust. Original plaster model. Rome
1819. H. 54cm.

A289 George Hilaro Barlow
1762-1848. Knighted 1803. Governor General of India 1805-07.
Governor of Madras 1807-12.
Bust. Original plaster model. Rome
1828. H. 63,5 cm. Marble version,
see A892.

A290 Karl von Seinsheim?
Ground floor, room 12.
1784-1864. Bavarian count.
Bust. Original plaster model. Rome
1818. H. 55,2 cm.

A291 Arthur Potocki
Ground floor, room 15.
1787-1832. Polish count.
Bust. Original plaster model. Rome
1829. H. 68 cm.

A292 Unknown Man
First floor, western corridor.
Bust. Original plaster model.
Rome c. 1816-19. H. 54,4 cm.

A293 Nicolaus Esterhazy
First floor, western corridor.
1765-1833. Hungarian prince.
Bust. Original plaster model.
Rome 1817. H. 53 cm.

A294 Henry Labouchère
First floor, western corridor.
1798-1869. British statesman, later
first Baron Taunton.
Bust. Original plaster model. Rome
1828. H. 65,9 cm.

A295 Stanislaw Kossakowski
1795-1872. Polish count, secretary
at the Russian Embassy in Rome
1819-27.
Bust. Original plaster model. Rome
1825. H. 58,8 cm. Marble version,
see A706.

A296 Unknown Man
First floor, southern corridor.
Bust. Original plaster model. Rome
c. 1824-30. H. 60,1 cm.

A297 Francis Basset?
First floor, southern corridor.
1747-1821. Baron de Dunstanville,
English political writer.
Bust. Original plaster model. Rome
1818. H. 56 cm.

A298 Thomas Hope
1769-1831. English art collector
and author.
Bust. Original plaster model. Rome
1817. H. 55,2 cm. Marble version,
see A823.

A299 George Agar Ellis
First floor, southern corridor.
1797-1833. English historical writer, later Baron Dover.
Bust. Original plaster model. Rome 1818. H. 50,6 cm.

A300 François Gabriel de Bray
First floor, southern corridor.
1765-1832. French by birth, entered Bavarian Service as a diplomat. Bavarian Count.
Bust. Original plaster model. Rome c. 1818-19. H. 51,2 cm.

A301 Michael Coronini-Cronberg
First floor, room 28.
1793-1876. Austrian count.
Bust. Original plaster model. Rome 1816. H. 55,5 cm.

A302 Ivan Vorontsov?
First floor, room 28.
1790-1856. Russian count.
Bust. Original plaster model. c. 1803-04. H. 53 cm.

A303 John Campbell?
Ground floor, northern corridor.
1796-1862. Lord Glenorchy, later Marquis of Breadalbane, M. P.
Bust. Original plaster model. Rome c. 1829. H. 70,4 cm.

A304 Yevdokia Ivanovna Golitsyn
Entrance hall.
1780-1850. Russian princess.
Bust. Marble version (Thorvaldsen) of the original plaster model executed 1803-04 in Rome. H. 73,1 cm.

A305 Unknown Lady
Ground floor, room 3.
Bust. Original plaster model.
Rome c. 1827-38. H. 48,6 cm.

A306 Unknown Lady
Ground floor, room 11.
Bust. Original plaster model.
Rome c. 1816-19. H. 55 cm.

A307 Jane Craufurd
Ground floor, room 18.
1798-1884. Daughter of the Scottish Baronet James Gregan Craufurd.
Bust. Original plaster model. Rome 1818. H. 53,6 cm. Marble version, see A898.

A308 Anne Bingham?
First floor, landing.
C. 1796-1850. Daughter of Richard Bingham, Earl of Lucan.
Bust. Original plaster model.
Rome c. 1816-17. H. 56,3 cm.

A309 Harriet Frances Pellew
First floor, northern corridor.
1794-1849. Née Webster, married to the English admiral Sir Fleetwood Pellew.
Bust. Original plaster model. Rome 1817. H. 55 cm.

A310 Marie Louise Playdeux?
First floor, northern corridor.
Mistress of Prince Nicolaus Esterhazy.
Bust. Original plaster model. Rome c. 1817-18. H. 55,3 cm.

A311 Elizabeth Vernon?
First floor, southern corridor.
1795-1838. Daughter of Richard Bingham, Earl of Lucan. Married to George Granville Vernon. From 1830 Lady Harcourt.
Bust. Original plaster model. Rome c. 1816-17. H. 53,5 cm.

A312 Wilhelmine Benigna Biron
First floor, southern corridor.
1781-1839. Duchess of Sagan.
Bust. Original plaster model.
Rome 1818. H. 58 cm.
See also A720 and A811.

A313 Georgina Bingham?
First floor, northern corridor.
1799-1849. Daughter of Richard
Bingham, Earl of Lucan.
Bust. Original plaster model.
Rome c. 1816-17. H. 53,5 cm.

A314 Unknown Child
First floor, room 30.
Bust. Plaster cast. The original
plaster model, Rome c. 1816-19.
H. 45 cm.

A315 Georgiana Elizabeth Russell
First floor, room 30.
C. 1810-1867. Daughter of John
Russell, sixth Duke of Bedford.
Bust. Preliminary work for A173.
Original plaster model. Rome 1815.
H. 42,2 cm.

A316 Jupiter Enthroned between Minerva and Nemesis
Ground floor, room 12.
Relief. Sketch model. Plaster.
Rome, probably 1822. H. 113 cm.
W. 457 cm. Executed in terracotta
by G. Borup in colossal size and in
1847 placed in the pediment of the
main facade of Christiansborg
Palace in Copenhagen, destroyed
by fire in 1884.

A317 Hercules Receiving the Draught of Immortality from Hebe
Entrance hall.
An Allegory of Strength.
Relief. Original plaster model.
Rome 1808. D. 147,5 cm. A
marble version was placed on the
facade of Christiansborg Palace,
Copenhagen, in 1825; it is now in
the passageway, "Kongeporten".

A318 Hygieia Feeding the Snake of Aesculapius
Entrance hall.
An Allegory of Health.
Relief. Original plaster model.
Rome 1808. D. 146,5 cm. A
marble version was placed on the
facade of Christiansborg Palace,
Copenhagen, in 1825; now in the
passageway "Kongeporten".

A319 Minerva Grants a Soul to Mankind Created by Prometheus
Entrance hall.
An Allegory of Wisdom.
Relief. Original plaster model.
Rome 1807-08. D. 147 cm. A
marble version was placed on the
facade of Christiansborg Palace,
Copenhagen, in 1825; it is now in
the passageway "Kongeporten".

A320 Nemesis Recites the Deeds of Men to Jupiter
Entrance Hall.
An Allegory of Justice.
Relief. Original plaster model. Ro-
me 1810. D. 147,5 cm. A marble
version was placed on the facade of
Christiansborg Palace, Copenhagen,
in 1825; it is now in the passageway
"Kongeporten".

A321 Hercules Receiving the Draught of Immortality from Hebe
Ground floor, room 6.
Relief. Marble version in reduced size of A317 (Rome 1808).
D. 81,5 cm.

A322 Hygieia Feeding the Snake of Aesculapius
Ground floor, room 6.
Relief. Marble version in reduced size of A318. (Rome l808).
D. 80,5 cm.

A323 Minerva Grants a Soul to Mankind Created by Prometheus
Ground floor, room 6.
Relief Marble version in reduced size of A319 (Rome 1807-08).
D. 80,5 cm.

A324 Nemesis Recites the Deeds of Men to Jupiter
Ground floor, room 6.
Relief. Marble version in reduced size of A320 (Rome 1810).
D. 80,5 cm.

A325 Minerva
Ground floor, room 10.
Relief. Original plaster model.
Rome c. 1836. D. 64 cm.

A326 Apollo
Ground floor, room 10.
Relief. Original plaster model.
Rome c. 1836. D. 65,5 cm.

A327 The Genius of Light with Pegasus
Ground floor, room 1.
Relief. Original plaster model.
Rome c. 1836. D. 67,5 cm.

A328 Clio, Muse of History
Ground floor, room 18.
Relief. Original plaster model.
Rome c. 1836. D. 64 cm.

A329 Euterpe, Muse of Music
Ground floor, room 18.
Relief. Original plaster model.
Rome c. 1836. D. 64 cm.

A330 Thalia, Muse of Comedy
Ground floor, room 18.
Relief. Original plaster model.
Rome c. 1836. D. 64,5 cm.

A331 Melpomene, Muse of Tragedy
Ground floor, room 18.
Relief. Original plaster model.
Rome c. 1836. D. 64,5 cm.

A332 Terpsichore, Muse of Dancing
Ground floor, room 18.
Relief. Original plaster model.
Rome c. 1836. D. 64,5 cm.

A333 Erato, Muse of Lyric and Love Poetry
Ground floor, room 18.
Relief. Original plaster model.
Rome c. 1836. D. 64 cm.

A334 Polyhymnia, Muse of Religious Poetry
Ground floor, room 18.
Relief. Original plaster model.
Rome c. 1836. D. 64 cm.

A335 Urania, Muse of Astronomy
Ground floor, room 18.
Relief. Original plaster model.
Rome c. 1836. D. 64 cm.

A336 Calliope, Muse of Epic Poetry
Ground floor, room 18.
Relief. Original plaster model.
Rome c. 1836. D. 64 cm.

A337 Mnemosyne, Mother of the Muses, and Harpocrates
Ground floor, room 18.
Relief. Original plaster model.
Rome c. 1836. D. 64,5 cm.

A338 The Hovering Graces
First floor, room 27.
Relief. Original plaster model.
Rome c. 1836. D. 65,5 cm.

A339 The Procession to Parnassus
First floor, northern corridor.
Apollo with Pegasus and the Genius of Light; the Graces and the Muses, accompanied by cupids; Homer led by the Genius of Poetry.
Relief. Original plaster model.
Rome 1832. H. 63,3 cm.
W. 490,5 cm.

A340 The Dance of the Muses on Helicon
Ground floor, room 3.
Apollo, the Muses, and the Graces.
Relief. Marble version of A341 (Rome 1816) executed by Christian Freund under the supervision of H. W. Bissen. H. 72,5 cm. W. 159 cm.

A341 The Dance of the Muses on Helicon
First floor, northern corridor.
Apollo, the Muses, and the Graces.
Relief. Original plaster model. Rome 1816. And adaptation of a relief

modelled in 1804 at Montenero.
H. 73,5 cm. W. 160 cm. Marble version, see A340. See also A705.

A342 The Muses of Tragedy and Comedy (Melpomene and Thalia)
Ground floor, room 20.
Relief. Original plaster model. Nysø 1843. D. 76 cm.

A343 Cupid Listening to the Song of Erato
Ground floor, room 13.
Relief. Marble version of the original plaster model executed 1830 in Rome. D. 56,5 cm.

A344 Apollo among the Shepherds
First floor, room 33.
Relief. Sketch model. Plaster.
Rome 1837. H. 30 cm. W. 177 cm.
An enlarged marble version was executed by Pietro Galli for the pediment of the Villa Carolina in Castel Gandolfo.

A345 Diana Beseeches Jupiter for Permission to Devote Herself to Hunting
First floor, room 26.
Relief. Original plaster model.
Inscribed: "Albert Thorvaldsen Nysøe d. 20. April 1840".
H. 71,5 cm. W. 81,5 cm.

A346 Mercury Brings the Infant Bacchus to Ino
First floor, room 24.
Relief. Original plaster model.
An adaptation of A347.
Rome, probably 1809.
H. 74,5 cm. W. 74 cm.

A347 Mercury Brings the Infant Bacchus to Ino
First floor, southern corridor.
Relief. Original plaster model.
Rome 1809. H. 49,5 cm. W. 50,7
cm. Marble version, see A796.

A348 Venus Rising from the Foam
Ground floor, room 4.
Relief. Original plaster model.
Rome 1809.
H. 42,3 cm. W. 38,5 cm.

A349 The Abduction of Ganymede
Relief. Original plaster model.
Rome 1833. H. 25,5 cm.
W. 20,3 cm.

A350 The Abduction of Ganymede
Relief. Original plaster model.
Rome 1833. H. 33,5 cm.
W. 47,5 cm.

A351 Hebe Gives Ganymede the Cup and Pitcher
Ground floor, room 14.
Relief Original plaster model. Rome
1833. H. 48,2 cm. W. 47 cm.

A352 Pan Teaching a Child Satyr to Play on a Reed Pipe
Ground floor, room 10.
Relief. Marble version of A353
(Rome 1831). H. 46,5 cm.
W. 78,3 cm.

A353 Pan Teaching a Child Satyr to Play on a Reed Pipe
First floor, southern corridor.
Relief. Original plaster model.
Rome 1831. H. 46,4 cm. W. 77,8
cm. Marble version, see A352.

A354 Bacchante and a Child Satyr
Ground floor, room 10.
Relief. Marble version of A355
(Rome 1833). H. 46,5 cm.
W. 78,3 cm.

A355 Bacchante and a Child Satyr
First floor, southern corridor.
Relief. Original plaster model.
Rome 1833. H. 47 cm. W. 78,8
cm. Marble version, see A354.

A356 Pan and a Hunting Nymph
First floor, southern corridor.
Relief Original plaster model. Rome
c. 1838. H. 67,2 cm. W. 58,2 cm.
Marble version, see A728.

A357 Satyr Dancing with a Bacchante
Ground floor, room 13.
Relief. Original plaster model. Nysø
1840-41. H. 63,5 cm. W. 72 cm.

A358 Satyr Dancing with a Bacchante
Ground floor, room 13.
Relief. Original plaster model. Nysø
1840-41. H. 65,7 cm. W. 74,5 cm.

A359 Victory Recording Deeds on a Shield
Ground floor, room 15.
Relief. Marble version of A360
(Rome c. 1830). H. 81,2 cm.
W. 62,5 cm .

A360 Victory Recording Deeds on a Shield

First floor, southern corridor.
Relief. Original plaster model.
Rome c. 1830. H. 81,5 cm. W.
63,5 cm. Originally modelled for a
pedestal for the bust of Napoleon I
(see A909), but never used. Marble
version, see A359.

A361 Victory Seated with a Sword and Helmet

Ground floor, western corridor.
Relief. Partly an original plaster
model. Rome 1830. H. 98 cm. W.
71,5 cm. Originally modelled for
the pedestal of the Potocki monument (see A155), but never used.

A362 Victory Standing with a Shield and Palm

Ground floor, room 15.
Relief. Original plaster model.
Rome c. 1830. H. 90 cm. W. 63
cm. Originally modelled for the pedestal of the Potocki monument
(see A155), but never used.

A363 Victory

Ground floor, southern corridor.
Relief. Original plaster model.
Rome 1830. H. 97,2 cm.
W. 65 cm.

A364 Nemesis in a Chariot, Attended by the Genii of Punishment and Reward

Ground floor, room 15.
Relief. Original plaster model.
Rome 1834. H. 97 cm. W. 187,7
cm. A marble version was placed in
the Memorial Chapel of Julius
Mylius, in the Villa Vigoni by Lake
Como.

A365 The Fates with the Thread of Life

Ground floor, room 13.
Relief. Marble version A366 (Rome
1833) executed 1864 by C. C.
Olsen under the supervision of H.
W. Bissen. H. 122 cm, W. 181 cm.

A366 The Fates with the Thread of Life

Ground floor, room 8.
Relief. Original plaster model.
Rome 1833. H. 71 cm. W. 106 cm.
Enlarged marble version, see A365.

A367 Night
See A901.

A368 Day
See A902.

A369 Night

First floor, northern corridor.
Relief. Original plaster model.
Rome 1815. D. 75 cm.
Marble version, see A901 and
A905.

A370 Day

First floor, northern corridor.
Relief. Original plaster model.
Rome 1815 (or an adaptation from
1817). D. 78 cm. Marble version,
see A902 and A906.

A371 Cupid Feeding Hygieia's Snake

Ground floor, room 3.
Relief. Marble version of A372
(Rome 1837). H. 80 cm. W. 57 cm.

A372 Cupid Feeding Hygieia's Snake

First floor, southern corridor.
Relief. Original plaster model.
Rome 1837. H. 76 cm. W. 55,5
cm. Marble version, see A371.

A373 Hygieia Crowned by Cupid (Love and Health)
First floor, room 23.
Relief. Original plaster model. Inscribed: "Nysøe d 24. April 1840".
H. 60,2 cm. W. 63 cm.

A374 The Graces Dancing
Ground floor, room 9.
Relief. Original plaster model.
H. 64 cm. W. 56 cm.

A375 The Graces with Cupid in Chains of Roses
Ground floor, room 3.
Relief. Marble version of A376 (Rome 1831). H. 39 cm. W. 72 cm.

A376 The Graces with Cupid in Chains of Roses
First floor, northern corridor.
Relief. Original plaster model.
Rome 1831. H. 37,3 cm. W. 71 cm. Marble version, see A375.

A377 Cupid in Heaven, on Jupiter's Eagle, with the Thunderbolt
Ground floor, room 16.
A377-A380 represent Cupid's dominion over the Four Elements, in this case Air.
Relief. Marble version of A381 (Rome 1828). H. 48,2 cm. W. 64 cm.

A378 Cupid on Earth, as the Lion Tamer, with Hercules' Club
Ground floor, room 16.
A377-A380 represent Cupid's dominion over the Four Elements, in this case Earth.
Relief Marble version of A382 (Rome 1828). H. 48,3 cm. W. 64,7 cm.

A379 Cupid at Sea, on a Dolphin, with Neptune's Trident
Ground floor, room 16.
A377-A380 represent Cupid's dominion over the Four Elements, in this case Water.
Relief Marble version of A383 (Rome 1828). H. 48,2 cm. W. 64,2 cm.

A380 Cupid in the Underworld, as the Tamer of Cerberus, with Pluto's Pitchfork
Ground floor, room 16.
A377-A380 represent Cupid's dominion over the Four Elements, in this case Fire.
Relief. Marble version of A384 (Rome 1828). H. 48,7 cm. W. 64,5 cm.

A381 Cupid in Heaven, on Jupiter's Eagle, with the Thunderbolt
First floor, northern corridor.
Relief. Original plaster model.
Rome 1828. H. 49 cm. W. 67 cm. Marble version, see A377.

A382 Cupid on Earth, as the Lion Tamer, with Hercules' Club
First floor, northern corridor.
Relief. Original plaster model.
Rome 1828. H. 49,5 cm. W. 65,5 cm. Marble version, see A378.

A383 Cupid at Sea, on a Dolphin, with Neptune's Trident
First floor, northern corridor.
Relief. Original plaster model.
Rome 1828. H. 48,3 cm. W. 64,1 cm. Marble version, see A379.

A384 Cupid in the Underworld, as the Tamer of Cerberus, with Pluto's Pitchfork

First floor, northern corridor.
Relief. Original plaster model.
Rome 1828. H. 48,7 cm. W. 66,5
cm. Marble version, see A380.

A385 Cupid on Jupiter's Eagle

First floor, southern corridor.
Relief. Preliminary work for A381.
Original plaster model. Rome 1828
H. 51,5 cm. W. 65 cm.

A386 Cupid on Jupiter's Eagle

First floor, southern corridor.
Relief. Preliminary work for A381.
Original plaster model. Rome 1828
H. 48 cm. W. 62,2 cm.

A387 Cupid with the Tamed Lion

First floor, southern corridor.
Relief. Preliminary work for A382.
Original plaster model. Rome 1828.
H. 42 cm. W. 62 cm.
Marble version, see A729.

A388 Cupid with the Tamed Lion

Ground floor, room 4.
Relief. Original plaster model.
Rome 1809. H. 53 cm.
W. 72,3 cm.

A389 Cupid Riding on a Lion

Ground floor, room 14.
Relief. Marble version of the original plaster model executed in 1831
in Rome. H. 58 cm. W. 66 cm.

A390 Cupid Riding on a Lion

First floor, southern corridor.
Relief. Plaster cast. The original
plaster model. Rome 1831.
H. 54 cm. W. 62,2 cm.
Marble version, see A389.

A391 Cupid Writes the Laws of Jupiter

Ground floor, room 14.
Relief. Marble version (Thorvaldsen) of A392 (Rome 1831). H. 46
cm. W. 68,5 cm.

A392 Cupid Writes the Laws of Jupiter

First floor, northern corridor.
Relief. Original plaster model.
Rome 1831. H. 44,2 cm. W. 67
cm. Marble version, see A391.

A393 Cupid Asks Jupiter and Juno that the Rose May Be Queen of Flowers

Ground floor, room 3.
Relief. Marble version of A394
(Rome 1831). H. 35 cm. W. 57 cm.

A394 Cupid Asks Jupiter and Juno that the Rose May Be Queen of Flowers

First floor, northern corridor.
Relief. Original plaster model.
Rome 1831. H. 33 cm. W. 55,5
cm. Marble version, see A393.
See also A878.

A395 Cupid and Ganymede Playing at Dice

Ground floor, room 16.
Relief. Marble version (Thorvaldsen) of the original plaster model
executed 1831 in Rome. H. 42,5
cm. W. 63 cm.

A396 Cupid Caressing the Faithful Dog
Ground floor, room 3.
Relief. Marble version of A399 (Rome 1831). H. 39 cm. W. 60 cm.

A397 Cupid Making a Net to Catch a Butterfly
Ground floor, room 3.
Relief. Marble version of A398 (Rome 1831) H. 39 cm. W. 60 cm.

A398 Cupid Caressing the Faithful Dog
First floor landing.
Relief. Original plaster model. Rome 1831. H. 39,8 cm. W. 59 cm. Marble version, see A396.

A399 Cupid Making a Net to Catch a Butterfly
First floor, landing.
Relief. Original plaster model. Rome 1831. H. 39,5 cm. W. 59,7 cm. Marble version, see A397.

A400 Cupid Sailing
First floor, southern corridor.
Relief. Original plaster model. Rome 1831. H. 26 cm. W. 47 cm.

A401 Cupid Sailing
First floor, room 25.
Relief. An adaptation of A400. Original plaster model. Rome 1831. H. 44,5 cm. W. 61,5 cm.

A402 Cupid Collecting Shells for a Necklace
Ground floor, room 8.
Relief. Original plaster model. Rome 1831. H. 35,5 cm. W. 50 cm.

A403 Cupid Charms Flowers from Stony Ground
Ground floor, room 8.
Relief. Original plaster model. Rome 1831. H. 38 cm. W. 52 cm.

A404 Cupid Sets Stone on Fire
First floor, southern corridor.
Relief. Original plaster model. Rome 1831. H. 50 cm. W. 37,2 cm.

A405 Cupid Holding out a Rose, and Concealing Thistles
First floor, room 22.
Relief Original plaster model. Rome 1837. H. 70 cm. W. 62,5 cm.

A406 Cupid Holding out a Rose, and Concealing Thistles
Ground floor, room 19.
Relief. An adaptation of A405. Original plaster model. Rome 1837. H. 58,3 cm. W. 44 cm.

A407 Cupid and Bacchus
Ground floor, room 10.
Relief. Marble version of A408, (Rome 1810?), probably executed in 1824 in Rome. H. 51,7 cm. W 89,7 cm.

A408 Cupid and Bacchus
First floor, southern corridor.
Relief Original plaster model. Rome, probably 1810. H. 53 cm. W. 83 cm. Marble version, see A407.

A410 Cupid with a Swan and Boys Picking Fruit
Ground floor, room 4.
An Allegory of Summer.
Relief Marble version of A411
(Montenero 1810 or Rome 1811).
H. 53,3 cm. W. 69,3 cm.

A411 Cupid with a Swan and Boys picking Fruit
First floor, northern corridor.
An Allegory of Summer.
Relief. Original plaster model.
Montenero 1810 or Rome 1811.
H. 57,2 cm. W. 69,5 cm. Marble
version, see A410.

A412 Cupid and the Youthful Bacchus Treading Grapes
Ground floor, room 4.
An Allegory of Autumn.
Relief. Marble version of A413
(Montenero 1810 or Rome 1811).
H. 51,5 cm. W. 67 cm.

A413 Cupid and the Youthful Bacchus Treading Grapes
First floor, northern corridor.
An Allegory of Autumn.
Relief Original plaster model. Montenero 1810 of Rome 1811. H. 50
cm. W. 69 cm. Marble version, see
A412.

A414 Cupid Received by Anacreon
See A827

A415 Cupid Received by Anacreon
First floor, northern corridor.
An Allegory of Winter.
Relief. Plaster cast. The original
plaster model, Rome 1823. H. 49,5
cm. W. 67 cm. Marble versions,
see A416 and A827.

A416 Cupid Received by Anacreon
Ground floor, room 10.
Relief. Marble. An adaptation of
A415. H. 54 cm. W. 90,3 cm.

A417 Cupid Stung by a Bee Complains to Venus
Ground floor, room 14.
Relief. Marble version (Thorvaldsen) of A780 (Rome 1809).
H. 49 cm. W. 53 cm.

A418 Cupid Stung by a Bee Complains to Venus
Ground floor, room 9.
Relief. An adaptation of A780.
Original plaster model. H. 70,5 cm.
W. 61 cm.

A419 Cupid's Arrows Forged in Vulcan's Smithy
Ground floor, room 9.
Relief Original plaster model.
Rome, probably 1810.
H. 74,5 cm. W. 130,3 cm.

A420 Venus, Mars, and Cupid in the Smithy of Vulcan
Ground floor, western corridor.
Relief. An adaptation of A419. Plaster, Mars an original plaster model,
the other figures plaster casts.
Rome, probably 1814. H. 75,7 cm.
W. 137 cm.

A421 Cupid Riding on a Swan
Ground floor, room 19.
Relief. Original plaster model.
Inscribed: "Nysøe d. 18 Novemb.
1840". D. 77,5 cm.

A422 Cupid on a Swan
Ground floor, room 12.
Relief. Original plaster model. Nysø
1810. H. 59 cm. W. 69,5 cm.

A423 Leda and the Swan
Ground floor, southern corridor.
Relief. Original plaster model. Inscribed: "Nysøe d 3 Febru .. 1841".
H. 68,5 cm. W. 99,2 cm.

A424 Shepherdess with a Nest of Cupids
Ground floor, room 14.
Relief. Marble version (Thorvaldsen) of A425 (Rome 1831).
Inscribed: "Thorvaldsen fecit".
H. 59,8 cm. W. 58,5 cm.

A425 Shepherdess with a Nest of Cupids
First floor, room 32.
Relief. Original plaster model.
Rome 1831. H. 57,5 cm. W. 58
cm. Marble version, see A424.

A426 The Ages of Love
Ground floor, room 2.
Relief. Marble version of the original plaster model executed in 1824
in Rome. H. 52 cm. W. 148 cm.
See also A427 and A739.

A427 The Ages of Love
First floor, room 33.
Relief. Sketch model. Plaster. Rome
1824. H. 40 cm. W. 123,5 cm.
Marble version, see A426.

A428 Cupid Leaves the Bed of the Sleeping Psyche
Ground floor, room 2.
Relief. Original plaster model. Nysø
1841. H. 50,5 cm. W. 60,5 cm.

A429 Psyche with the Lamb Approaches the Sleeping Cupid
Ground floor, room 2.
Relief. Original plaster model. Nysø
1841. H. 52 cm. W. 63 cm.

A430 Cupid Revives the Swooning Psyche
Relief. Marble version of A431
(Montenero 1810). H. 57,5 cm. W.
90,5 cm. See also A865.

A431 Cupid Revives the Swooning Psyche
First floor, southern corridor.
Relief. Original plaster model.
Montenero 1810. H. 48,8 cm. W.
80 cm. Marble version, see A430
and A866.

A432 Psyche Carried to Heaven by Mercury
First floor, room 31.
Relief. Original plaster model.
D. 58 cm.

A433-A448 A series of reliefs representing the legend of Cupid and Psyche as told by Apuleius
First floor, western corridor.
Reliefs. Plaster casts of reliefs modelled 1838 from Thorvaldsen's
drawings by Pietro Galli for the
now demolished Palazzo Torlonia,
Rome. H. 26,5 cm. W. 22 cm.

A433 Venus Asking Cupid to Arouse Psyche's Love for some Worthless Being.
See above.

A434 Cupid Gazing at the Sleeping Psyche
See above.

A435 Psyche's Father Consulting the Oracle
See above.

A436 Zephyr and Psyche
See above.

A437 Cupid Approaching the Sleeping Psyche
See above.

A438 Cupid Leaving the Bed of the Sleeping Psyche
See above.

A439 Psyche and her Sisters
See above.

A440 Psyche Trying to Detain Cupid
See above.

A441 Psyche and Pan
See above.

A442 Venus Commanding Psyche to Fetch Water from the River Styx
See above.

A443 Jupiter's Eagle Bringing Psyche Water from the River Styx
See above.

A444 Psyche and Charon
See above.

A445 Psyche and Cerberus
See above.

A446 Cupid Reviving the Swooning Psyche
See above.

A447 Psyche Carried to Heaven by Mercury
See above.

A448 Psyche and Cupid Reunited
See above.

A449 Cupid and Psyche, or Goodbye to Nysø
Relief. Plaster cast. Inscribed (reversed): "Nysøe [d 24 May 1841]". The original plaster model, Nysø 1841. H. 38,5 cm. W. 38,5 cm.

A450 Cupid and Psyche
First floor, landing.
Relief. Original plaster model. Nysø 1840. H. 73 cm. W. 60 cm. See A805-08.

A451 Cupid and Hymen
Ground floor, room 11.
Relief. Marble version of A452 (Nysø 1840), executed in 1842-44 in Thorvaldsen's studio in Rome. H. 75,3 cm. W. 61 cm.

A452 Cupid and Hymen
First floor, landing.
Relief. Original plaster model. Nysø 1840. H. 73 cm. W. 59 cm. Marble version, see A451.

A453 Cupid Garlands Hymen's Torches
Relief. Original plaster model. Copenhagen 1840. D. 47,8 cm.

A454 Cupid and Hymen Spinning the Thread of Life
Ground floor, room 16.
Relief. Marble version of A455
(Rome 1831), executed 1832-34.
H. 42,5 cm. W. 57 cm.

A455 Cupid and Hymen Spinning the Thread of Life
First floor, northern corridor.
Relief. Original plaster model.
Rome 1831. H. 12 cm. W. 59 cm.
Marble version, see A454.

A456 Cupid's Swansong
First floor, landing.
Relief. Original plaster model. Nysø
1843. D. 93,5 cm.

A457 Hymen
Ground floor, room 9.
Relief. Plaster cast. The original
plaster model A731, Nysø 1843.
D. 94 cm.

A458-A479 A series of reliefs representing the Metamorphoses of Ovid
First floor, northern corridor.
Reliefs. Plaster casts of reliefs modelled in 1838 from Thorvaldsen's
drawings by Pietro Galli for the
now demolished Palazzo Torlonia,
Rome.

A458 The Flight of Latona
See above. H. 32,5 cm. W. 25,3 cm.

A459 Diana with her Hind
See above. H. 33,7 cm. W. 25 cm.

A460 Diana Surprised by Actaeon
See above. H. 33 cm. W. 24,6 cm.

A461 Actaeon Torn by his Dogs
See above. H. 32,8 cm. W. 25 cm.
See also A779.

A462 Diana Killing Orion
See above. H. 33,5 cm. W. 25 cm.

A463 Orion Dying
See above. H. 33 cm. W. 23,5 cm.

A464 Chione and Daedalion
See above. H. 33,5 cm. W. 25,3 cm.

A465 Cupid Leading Diana to Endymion
See above. H. 33 cm. W. 25 cm.

A466 Endymion Sleeping
See above. H. 32,5 cm. W. 24,8 cm.

A467 Nymph with Bow
See above, H. 33 cm. W. 24,5 cm.

A468 Nymph with Arrow
See above. H. 33,5 cm. W. 24,5 cm.

A469 Nymph and a Young Girl
See above. H. 33,4 cm. W. 24,7 cm.

A470 Nymph with Torch
See above. H. 34 cm. W. 24,4 cm.

A471 Hunting Nymph
See above. H. 33,5 cm. W. 24 cm.

A472 Callisto
See above. H. 33,4 cm. W. 24,8 cm.

A473 Atalanta
See above. H. 33 cm. W 21,8 cm.

A474 Meleager and the Calydonian Boar
See above. H. 32,9 cm. W. 25,7 cm.

A475 Hero with a Slain Lion
See above. H. 34 cm. W. 24,2 cm.

A476 Adonis
See above. H. 31,4 cm. W 24,8 cm.

A477 Narcissus and Cupid
See above. H. 32,5 cm. W. 24,2 cm.

A478 Apollo and Daphne
See above. H. 34,5 cm. W. 22,5 cm.

A479 Pan with Syrinx and
Cupid
See above. H. 33,9 cm. W. 26,2 cm.

A480 The Centaur Nessus
Embracing the Struggling
Deianira
Ground floor, room 17.
Relief. Marble version (Thorvaldsen) of A481 (Rome 1814).
H. 103,5 cm. W. 127,5 cm.

A481 The Centaur Nessus
Embracing the Struggling
Deianira
Main staircase.
Relief. Original plaster model.
Rome 1814. H. 102 cm. W. 123
cm. Marble version, see A480.

A482 Hylas Stolen by the
Water Nymphs
Ground floor, room 19.
Relief. Marble version of A483
(Rome 1831). H. 40,7 cm.
W. 76 cm.

A483 Hylas Stolen by the
Water Nymphs
First floor, northern corridor.
Relief. Original plaster model.
Rome 1831. H. 40 cm. W. 76,5
cm. Marble version, see A482

A484 Hylas Stolen by the
Water Nymphs
Ground floor, room 14.
Relief. Marble version of A485.
(Rome 1833). H. 68 cm.
W. 109,5 cm.

A485 Hylas Stolen by the
Water Nymphs
First floor, northern corridor.
Relief. Original plaster model.
Rome 1833. H. 65 cm. W. 108,5
cm. Marble version, see A484.

A486 Perseus on Pegasus
Rescuing Andromeda
Ground floor, room 7.
Relief. Plaster cast. The original
plaster model A742, Nysø 1839.
D. 75,5 cm.

A487 The Sea-Goddess
Thetis Dipping her Son
Achilles in the River Styx
Ground floor, western corridor.
Relief. Original plaster model.
Rome 1837. H. 97,5 cm.
W. 136 cm.

A488 The Centaur Chiron
Teaching Achilles to Throw a
Spear
Main staircase.
Relief. Original plaster model.
Rome 1837. H. 102 cm. W. 124
cm. Marble version, see A798.

A489 Briseis Led away from
Achilles by Agamemnon's
Heralds
Ground floor, room 5.
Relief. Marble version of A490
(Rome 1803), executed 1865 by
Christian Freund under the super-
vision of H. W. Bissen. H. 114 cm.
W. 239 cm.

A490 Briseis Led away from Achilles by Agamemnon's Heralds

First floor, southern corridor.
Relief. Original plaster model.
Rome 1803. H. 116 cm. W. 236,5
cm. Marble version, see A489.

A491 Briseis Led away from Achilles by Agamemnon's Heralds

Ground floor, southern corridor.
Relief. An adaptation of A490. Original plaster model. Rome 1837.
H. 71 cm. W. 135 cm.

A492 Priam Pleads with Achilles for Hector's Body

First floor, southern corridor.
Relief. Original plaster model.
Rome 1815. H. 93,5 cm. W. 193,5
cm. Marble version, see A775.

A493 Achilles Binds the Wounds of Patroclus

Ground floor, room 5.
Relief. Marble version of A494
(Rome 1837). D. 67,5 cm.

A494 Achilles Binds the Wounds of Patroclus

First floor, northern corridor.
Relief. Original plaster model.
Rome 1837. D. 64,7 cm. Marble
version, see A493.

A495 Achilles with the Dying Amazon Penthesilea

Ground floor, room 5.
Relief. Marble version of A496,
(Rome 1837). D. 67 cm.

A496 Achilles with the Dying Amazon Penthesilea

First floor, northern corridor.
Relief. Original plaster model.
Rome 1837. D. 64,7 cm. Marble
version, see A494.

A497 Minerva Awarding Ulysses the Arms of Achilles

Ground floor, room 9.
Relief. Marble version of A498
(Rome 1831). Probably executed
1832-33. H. 65,5 cm.
W. 121,5 cm.

A498 Minerva Awarding Ulysses the Arms of Achilles

First floor, northern corridor.
Relief. Original plaster model.
Rome 1831. H. 63,2 cm. W. 119,2
cm. Marble version, see A497.

A499 Hector with Paris and Helen

First floor, northern corridor.
Relief. Original plaster model.
Rome 1809. H. 69,7 cm. W. 93
cm. Marble version, see A774.

A500 Hector with Paris and Helen

Ground floor, southern corridor.
Relief. Original plaster model.
Rome 1837. H. 84 cm. W. 165 cm.

A501 Hector's Farewell to Andromache

First floor, southern corridor.
Relief. Original plaster model.
Rome 1836 or 1837. H. 92,5 cm.
W. 182,3 cm. Marble version,
see A776.

A502 Homer Singing for the People

Ground floor, room 7.
Relief. Original plaster model.
Rome 1836-37. H. 97,7 cm.
W. 198 cm.

A503 Alexander the Great's Triumphal Entry into Babylon

Entrance hall.
Frieze. Plaster cast. The original plaster model executed in 1812 in Rome for the Quirinal Palace on the occasion of the expected arrival of Napoleon I. H. 106,5 cm. W. 3446 cm.

A504 Alexander the Great in his Triumphal Chariot Greeted by the Goddess of Peace

Ground floor, western corridor.
Relief. A variation of the central section of the Alexander Frieze A503. Original plaster model. Rome, probably 1818. H. 116,5 cm. W. 290,2 cm.

A505 Alexander the Great's Triumphal Entry into Babylon

Ground floor, southern corridor.
Frieze, a variation of A503 (Rome 1812). Plaster cast. H. 111 cm. W. 4026 cm. A marble version was executed between 1818 and 1827 for Count Sommariva's villa by Lake Como (Villa Carlotta). There are slight differences between A505 and the marble version.

A506 Woman Letting a Boy Ride a Ram

Ground floor, western corridor.
Relief. Plaster cast. The original plaster model, Rome 1831. H. 110,5 cm. W. 126,5 cm. Modelled as an extension to the marble version of the Alexander Frieze at Christiansborg Palace in Copenhagen, partly destroyed by fire in 1884. See A831-50.

A507 Four Babylonians with Horses

Ground floor, western corridor.
Relief. Original plaster model.
Rome 1831. H. 110,5 cm. W. 200 cm. Modelled as an extension to the marble version of the Alexander Frieze at Christiansborg Palace in Copenhagen, partly destroyed by fire in 1884. See A831-50.

A508 Alexander the Great's Triumphal Entry into Babylon

First floor, western corridor.
Frieze. Reduced marble version with alterations of A503 (Rome 1812), begun in 1822 by Pietro Galli. H. 55,5 cm. W. 2294,5 cm.

A509 Alexander the Great in his Triumphal Chariot

First floor, western corridor.
Relief, a variation of the central section of A508. Marble version, probably of A712. H. 58 cm. W. 110 cm.

A510 Trading-Post by the River

First floor, western corridor.
Relief. Original plaster model. H. 55,2 cm. W. 100,3 cm. Modelled as an extension to the Alexander Frieze and used in the marble version A508.

A511 Mother and her Children with Sheep
First floor, western corridor.
Relief. Plaster. Partly an original model. H. 55,2 cm. W. 116 cm. Modelled as an extension to the Alexander Frieze and used in the marble version A508.

A512 Youth Leading a Horse
First floor, western corridor.
Relief. Original plaster model. Rome, probably 1829. H. 55 cm. W. 65 cm. Modelled as an extension to the Alexander Frieze A508, but not used.

A513 Warrior Leading a Horse
First floor, western corridor.
Relief. Original plaster model. Rome 1831. H. 55 cm. W. 75 cm. Modelled as an extension to the Alexander Frieze A508, but not used.

A514 Alexander the Great Induced by Thais to Set Fire to Persepolis
Ground floor, room 15.
Relief. Marble version of A515 (Rome 1832) executed in 1865 by B. L. Bergslien and C. C. Olsen under the supervision of H. W. Bissen. H. 95 cm. W. 198 cm.

A515 Alexander the Great Induced by Thais to Set Fire to Persepolis
First floor, southern corridor.
Relief. Original plaster model. Rome 1832. H. 94 cm. W. 197,5 cm. Marble version, see A514.

A516 Alexander the Great Induced by Thais to Set Fire to Persepolis
Ground floor, southern corridor.
Relief. An adaptation of A515. Original plaster model. Rome 1837. H. 83 cm. W. 197 cm.

A517 Art and the Lightbringing Genius: A Genio Lumen
Ground floor, room 1.
Relief. Probably a preliminary work for A518. Original plaster model. Rome 1808 (?). H. 50,5 cm. W. 66, 5 cm.

A518 Art and the Lightbringing Genius: A Genio Lumen
First floor, southern corridor.
Relief. Original plaster model. Rome 1808. H. 103 cm. W. 136 cm. Marble version, see A828.

A519 The Genius of Light
Relief. Original plaster model. Nysø 1841. D. 31 cm. Designed for a medal, *Ingenio et Arti*, to be awarded to distinguished scientists and artists, instituted by Christian VIII.

A520 The Genius of Painting
Main staircase.
Relief. Original plaster model. Inscribed: "Nysø d' 21 Juli 1843". D. 93,5 cm.

A521 The Genius of Architecture
Main staircase.
Relief. Original plaster model. Inscribed: "Nysø d' 3 Decemb. 1843". D. 96 cm.

A522 The Genius of Sculpture
Main staircase.
Relief. Original plaster model. Inscribed: "Nysø d ...Juli 1843".
D. 93 cm.

A523 The Genius of Sculpture
Main staircase.
Relief. Original plaster model. Inscribed: "Kjøbenhavn d. 8 Marts 1844". D. 94 cm.

A524 The Genius of Sculpture Seated on the Shoulder of the Statue of Jupiter
Basement, room 45.
Chalk-sketch on a slate for a relief.
Copenhagen 1844. H. 109 cm. W. 109 cm. Thorvaldsen's last sketch.

A525 The Genii of Painting, Architecture, and Sculpture
Ground floor, room 18.
Relief. Original plaster model. Nysø 1843. D. 78 cm.

A526 The Genius of Poetry
Ground floor, northern corridor.
Relief, the first version of the relief A136 for the base of the Schiller monument. Original plaster model Rome 1835. H. 76 cm. W. 116 cm.

A527 The Genius of Poetry
First floor, landing.
Relief. Original plaster model. Inscribed: "Kjøbeha ... 24 Ap. 4".
(after Thorvaldsen's death). Copenhagen 1844. D. 97,5 cm.

A528 The Genii of Poetry and Harmony
Ground floor, room 20.
Relief. Original plaster model. Inscribed "Nysøe 30 Juli 1843".
D. 77,5 cm.

A529 The Genius of Peace and Freedom
Ground floor, southern corridor.
Relief. Original plaster model.
Copenhagen 1844. H. 75 cm.
W. 190,5 cm.

A530 The Genius of Government
Entrance hall.
Relief, modelled for the equestrian statue of Maximilian I in Munich (see A128), but not used. Original plaster model. Rome 1837.
H. 97,5 cm. W. 151,5 cm.

A531 The Genius of Justice
Entrance hall.
Relief, modelled for the equestrian statue of Maximilian I in Munich (see A128), but not used. Original plaster model Rome 1837. H. 97,2 cm. W. 154 cm.

A532-A545 A series of reliefs representing Genii of the Arts and Crafts
First floor, northern corridor.
Reliefs. Plaster casts of reliefs modelled 1838 from Thorvaldsen's drawings by Pietro Galli for the now demolished Palazzo Torlonia, Rome. H. 27 cm. W. 19 cm.

A532 The Genius of Poetry
See above.

A533 The Genius of Tragedy
See above.

A534 The Genius of Comedy
See above.

A535 The genius of Music
See above.

A536 The Genius of Dancing
See above

A537 The Genius of Government
See above.

A538 The Genius of War
See above.

A539 The Genius of Navigation
See above.

A540 The Genius of Trade
See above.

A541 The Genius of Medicine
See above.

A542 The Genius of Gardening
See above.

A543 The Genius of Agriculture
See above.

A544 The Genius of Astronomy
See above.

A545 The Genius of Religion
See above.

A546 Seven Genii
First floor, room 33.
The Genii of Architecture, Sculpture, Painting, Fishing, Hunting, Agriculture, and Gardening. Relief. Plaster cast. H. 38,5 cm. W. 55,5 cm. See note above A532. For the last two genii, see also A543 and A542.

A547 Six Genii
First floor, room 33.
The genii of Dancing, Government, War, Navigation, Trade (see A536-A540), and Justice. Relief. Plaster cast. H. 36 cm. W. 53, 5 cm. See note above A532.

A548 The Genius of the New Year
Ground floor, room 1.
Relief. Plaster cast. The original plaster model, Nysø 1840. D. 57 cm.

A549 Justitia
First floor, southern corridor.
Relief. Plaster cast. The original plaster model, Nysø 1841. H. 82,6 cm. W. 59 cm.

A550 Denmark Praying for the King
Relief. Design for a medal on the occasion of the accession of Christian VIII. Original plaster model. Inscribed: "Gud velsigne Kongen". (God Save the King). Copenhagen 1839. D. 49 cm.

A551 Adam and Eve with Cain and Abel
Ground floor, northern corridor.
Relief. Original plaster model. Rome 1838. H. 100 cm. W. 149 cm.

A552 Adam and Eve with Cain and Abel
First floor, room 33.
Relief. Sketch model for A551. Plaster. Rome 1837 or 1838. H. 35 cm. W. 36,4 cm.

A553 Rebecca and Eliezer by the Well
Ground floor, room 11.
Relief. Original plaster model.
Inscribed: "Nysøe d. 26 Janua(r)
1841". H. 94 cm. W. 183,3 cm.

A554 The Judgement of Solomon
First floor, room 33.
Relief. Sketch model. Plaster. Rome
1835. H. 39,5 cm. W. 199 cm. Modelled for a projected relief for the
pediment of the City Hall and
Court House of Copenhagen.

A555 Baptismal Font
First floor, room 28.
The reliefs of the four sides represent: The Baptism of Christ, The
Virgin with Jesus and Saint John as
Children, Christ Blessing the
Children, and Three Hovering
Angels, symbolizing Faith, Hope,
and Charity.
Square font with reliefs. Original
plaster model (except for the gar-
land, which is a cast). Rome 1805-
07. H. 77,8 cm. W. 72,5 cm. The
first marble version in the church
of Brahetrolleborg, Funen. Later
marble versions in the Cathedral of
Reykjavik, Iceland, and the Church
of the Holy Ghost, Copenhagen.

A556 The Virgin with Jesus and Saint John as Children
First floor, northern corridor.
Relief. A variation of the relief on
A555. Original plaster model.
Rome 1806. H. 57 cm. W. 52 cm.

A557 The Baptism of Christ
Ground floor, room 21.
Relief. Plaster cast. The original
plaster model, Copenhagen 1820.
H. 95 cm. W. 223,5 cm. Marble
version in the Church of Our Lady,
Copenhagen. See also A730.

A558 The Institution of Eucharist
Ground floor, room 21.
Relief. Plaster cast. The original
plaster model, Copenhagen 1820.
H. 97,5 cm. W. 224 cm. Marble
version in The Church of Our
Lady, Copenhagen.

A559 Christ's Entry into Jerusalem
The Christ Hall.
Frieze. Original plaster model. Nysø
1839-40. H. 64,2 cm. W. 747 cm.
A preliminary work for the frieze
above the main entrance of The
Church of Our Lady, Copenhagen.

A560 Christ on the Road to Calvary
The Christ Hall.
Frieze. Original plaster model. Nysø
1839-40. H. 66,5 cm. W. 758,5
cm. A preliminary work for the
frieze in the choir of the Church of
Our Lady, Copenhagen.

A561 The Resurrection of Christ
First floor, room 33.
Sketch model. Plaster cast. The ori-
ginal plaster model, Rome 1835.
H. 40 cm. W. 189,5 cm. Modelled
for a projected relief for the pedi-
ment of the Palace Chapel in
Copenhagen.

A562 Christ and the Two Disciples at Emmaus
First floor, northern corridor.
Relief. Original plaster model.
Rome 1818. H. 63 cm. W. 28,5
cm. Executed in silver for the
tabernacle on the high altar of SS.
Annunziata, Florence.

A563 Christ and the Two Disciples at Emmaus
Ground floor, room 21.
Relief. Plaster cast, probably of a
relief modelled 1839 at Nysø as an
altarpiece for Stavreby church near
Præstø. Inscribed: "Thorvald".
H. 120 cm. W. 153,5 cm.
Purchased 1845.

A564 Christ Assigns the Leadership of the Church to Saint Peter
The Christ Hall.
Relief. Plaster cast of the marble
version used as an antependium in
the chapel at the Villa Poggio Imperiale, Florence. The original plaster
model A565, Rome 1818. H. 64,5
cm. W. 181 cm.

A565 Christ Assigns the Leadership of the Church to Saint Peter
First floor, northern corridor.
Relief. Original plaster model.
Rome 1818. H. 62,5 cm. W. 179,5
cm. A marble version used as an
antependium in the chapel at the
Villa Poggio Imperiale, Florence.

A566 Christ Blessing the Children
First floor, room 33.
Relief. Plaster cast. The original
plaster model, Nysøe 1839.
H. 43,5 cm. W. 74,5 cm.

A567 Jesus as a Child in the Temple
Ground floor, eastern corridor.
Relief. Original plaster model. In-
scribed: "Nysøe d. 8 Marts 1841".
H. 84 cm. W. 72 cm.

A568 Christ and the Woman of Samaria at the Well
Ground floor, eastern corridor.
Relief. Original plaster model.
Inscribed: "Nysøe d. 10 Februar
1841". H. 77,5 cm. W. 70 cm.

A569 The Annunciation
The Christ Hall.
Relief. Original plaster model.
Inscribed: "Roma 20 Marzo 1842".
H. 65,5 cm. W. 125 cm.

A570 The Adoration of the Shepherds
The Christ Hall.
Relief. Original plaster model.
Inscribed: "Rom l. Januar 1842".
H. 65 cm. W. 123 cm.

A571 The Flight into Egypt
First floor, northern corridor.
Relief. Original plaster model.
Rome 1842. H. 68,7 cm.
W. 122,5 cm.

A572 Jesus as a Child in the Temple
The Christ Hall.
Relief. Original plaster model. In-
scribed: "Roma Maggio 1842".
H. 66,5 cm. W. 123 cm.

A573 The Baptism of Christ
The Christ Hall.
Relief. Original plaster model.
Inscribed: "agusto 184(2)". Rome
1842. H. 66 m. W. 125 cm.

A574 Christ's Entry into Jerusalem
First floor, room 34.
Relief. Original plaster model.
Rome 1842. H. 65,5 cm. W. 94,5 cm.

A575 Matthew
Ground floor, northern corridor.
Relief. Marble version of A579 (Rome 1833), executed in Thorvaldsen's studio in Rome between 1833 and 1835. D. 53,2 cm.

A576 Mark
Ground floor, northern corridor.
Relief. Marble version of A580 (Rome 1833), executed in 1834 in Thorvaldsen's studio in Rome. D. 53,5 cm.

A577 Luke
Ground floor, northern corridor.
Relief. Marble version of A581 (Rome 1833), executed 1834 in Thorvaldsen's studio in Rome. D. 53 cm.

A578 John
Ground floor, northern corridor.
Relief. Marble version of A582 (Rome 1833), executed between 1833 and 1835, in Thorvaldsen's studio in Rome. D. 53 cm.

A579 Matthew
First floor, northern corridor.
Relief. Original plaster model.
Rome 1833. D. 53 cm. Marble version, see A575.

A580 Mark
First floor, northern corridor.
Relief. Original plaster model. Rome 1833. D. 53 cm. Marble version, see A576.

A581 Luke
First floor, northern corridor.
Relief. Design for a medal for the Accademia di San Luca. Original plaster model. Rome 1833. D. 53 cm. Marble version, see A577.

A582 John
First floor, northern corridor.
Relief. Original plaster model.
Rome 1833. D. 53 cm. Marble version, see A578.

A583 St. Luke Writing his Gospel
Ground floor, northern corridor.
Relief. Original plaster model.
D. 50,5 cm.

A584 St. Luke as the First Christian Painter
Ground floor, northern corridor.
Relief. Original plaster model.
D. 53 cm.

A585 Angels Singing
Ground floor, room 2.
Relief. Marble version of A586 (Rome 1833). H. 38 cm. W. 42,5 cm.

A586 Angels Singing
First floor, northern corridor.
Relief. Original plaster model.
Rome 1833. H. 36,5 cm. W 40 cm. Marble version, see A585.

A587 Angels Playing
Ground floor, room 2.
Relief. Marble version of A588 Rome 1833). H. 39,2 cm. W. 43 cm.

A588 Angels Playing
First floor, northern corridor.
Relief. Original plaster model.
Rome 1833. H. 37 cm. W. 40 cm. Marble version, see A587.

A589 Christmas Joy in Heaven
Ground floor, northern corridor.
Relief. Plaster cast. The original plaster model, Nysø 1842. D. 101 cm. Marble version, see A855.

A590 Hovering Angels with Flowers and Garlands
First floor, northern corridor.
Relief. Original plaster model. Rome 1833. H. 35,5 cm. W. 64,5 cm. A bronze cast on the High Altar of the Novara Cathedral.

A591 Hovering Angels with Flowers and Garlands
First floor, northern corridor.
Relief. Original plaster model. Rome 1833. H. 38,5 cm. W. 62,5 cm. A bronze cast on the High Altar of The Novara Cathedral.

A592 Three Cupids with a Garland
First floor, northern corridor.
Relief. Original plaster model. (Copenhagen 1820?). H. 25,5 cm. W. 77 cm. A marble version on the chimney-piece A735.

A593 Angel of the Last Judgement
Ground floor, eastern corridor.
Relief. Original plaster model. Rome 1842. H. 98 cm. W. 67 cm. See also A908.

A594 Angel of the Last Judgement
Ground floor, northern corridor.
Relief. Original plaster model. Rome 1842. H. 79 cm. W. 48 cm.

A595 Angel of the Last Judgement
Ground floor, northern corridor.
Relief. Original plaster model. Rome 1842. H. 79,5 cm. W. 48 cm.

A596 The Child's Guardian Angel
Ground floor, The Christ Hall.
Relief. Original plaster model. Copenhagen 1838. H. 69,3 cm. W. 49,5 cm. See also A907. A marble version on the school collection box in the Church of our Lady, Copenhagen.

A597 Christian Charity
Ground floor, The Christ Hall.
Relief. Marble version of A598 (Rome 1810). H. 70 cm. W. 47 cm.

A598 Christian Charity
First floor, room 32.
Relief. Original plaster model. Rome 1810. H. 67,5 cm. W. 48 cm. Marble versions A597 and on the alms box in the Church of Our Lady, Copenhagen.

A599 Christian Charity United with Faith and Hope
Ground floor, room 21.
Relief. Original plaster model. Rome 1836. H. 45,5 cm. W. 85 cm.

A600 Minerva Protecting Virtue and Revealing Vice
Entrance hall.
Relief. Original plaster model. Rome 1818. H. 76 cm. W. 60,7 cm. A bronze cast on the base of the Maitland monument on Zakynthos (see A258).

A601 The Graces Listening to Cupid's Song
Ground floor, room 20.
Relief. Marble version executed in 1836 by J. Scholl in Thorvaldsen's studio in Rome. The original plaster model, Rome 1821. H. 125,5 cm. W. 101,5 cm. See also A602 and A629.

A602 The Graces Listening to Cupid's Song
First floor, southern corridor.
Relief. Plaster cast, probably of the original plaster model executed 1821 in Rome. H. 124,5 cm. W. 101 cm. Marble versions A602 and on the Andrea Appiani monument in the Palazzo di Brera, Milan. See also A629.

A603 Hans Madsen, Priest of Svanninge, tells Johan Rantzau of the Enemy's Plans
Ground floor, western corridor.
Relief. Original plaster model. Inscribed: "Nysøe den 5 Marts 1841". H. 137,5 cm. W. 99 cm. A bronze cast in Svanninge church, Funen.

A604 Genius of the Abolition of Villeinage
First floor, room 33.
Relief. Original plaster model. Inscribed: "Kjøbenhavn 12 Debr. 1842.". H. 59 cm. W. 41 cm. See also A809. Executed in marble by C. F. Holbech in Thorvaldsen's studio in Rome and placed on the monument to Frederik VI near Skanderborg in 1845.

A605 Genius of the Establishment of Provincial Consultative Chambers
First floor, room 33.
Relief. Original plaster model. Copenhagen 1842-43. H. 59 cm. W. 41 cm. Executed in marble by C. F. Holbech in Thorvaldsen's studio in Rome and placed on the monument to Frederik VI near Skanderborg in 1845.

A606 Genius of the Rule of Justice
First floor, room 33.
Relief. Original plaster model. Copenhagen 1841-43. H. 59 cm. W. 41 cm. Executed in marble by C. F. Holbech in Thorvaldsen's studio in Rome and placed on the monument to Frederik VI near Skanderborg in 1845.

A607 Genius of the Protection of the Arts and Sciences
First floor, room 33.
Relief. Original plaster model. Inscribed: "Kjøbenhavn den 6 Marts 1843". H. 59 cm. W. 41 cm. Executed in marble by C. F. Holbech in Thorvaldsen's studio in Rome and placed on the monument to Frederik VI near Skanderborg in 1845.

A608 Genius of the Abolition of Villeinage
Relief, preliminary work for A604. Plaster cast. The original plaster model, Copenhagen 1842. H. 62 cm. W. 44 cm.

A609 Personifications of Justice and Strength
First floor, room 33.
Relief, preliminary work for A606. Original plaster model. Inscribed: "Kjøbenhavn d:9 Januar 1843". H. 59 cm. W 41,5 cm.

A610 Genii Strewing Flowers on the Symbols of the Arts and Sciences

Relief, preliminary work for A607. Original plaster model. Inscribed: "Kjøbenhavn den 15.Januar 1843". H. 59,5 cm. W. 42 cm.

A611 Raphael between the Genius of Light and the Goddess of Victory

Ground floor, western corridor. Relief. Original plaster model. Rome 1833. H. 91,5 cm. W. 129 cm. Intended for Raphael's tomb in the Pantheon in Rome, but not used.

A612 Cardinal Consalvi Restores the Papal Provinces to Pius VII

Ground floor, western corridor. Relief. Original plaster model. Rome 1825. H. 58 cm. W. 120,7 cm. A marble version on Consalvi's tomb in the Pantheon in Rome. See also A271.

A613 Tobias Heals his Blind Father

Ground floor, northern corridor. Relief. Original plaster model. Rome 1828. H. 103 cm. W. 197 cm. A marble version on the tomb of the Italian oculist Vacca Berlinghieri (1771-1826) in Campo Santo, Pisa.

A614 Tomb for Auguste Böhmer

Ground floor, room 12. Three reliefs. Original plaster models. Rome 1811-12.
1. The Departed Tends her Sick Mother. H. 79 cm. W. 61 cm.
2. Nemesis. H. 78,5 cm. W. 47 cm.

3. The Genius of Death. H. 79 cm. W. 45,5 cm.
The Marble versions A700-702 and the bust A703 were intended for the tomb of August Böhmer (1785-1800) in Bocklet, but never placed.

A615 Tomb for Philipp Bethmann-Hollweg

Ground floor, room 12. Three reliefs. Original plaster models. Rome 1814.
1. The Deceased's Brother Bringing him the Emperor of Austria's Reward. H. 90 cm. W. 140 cm.
2. The Sorrowing Mother and Sister of the Deceased. H. 89, 5 cm. W. 93,5 cm.
3. Nemesis Recording his Deed and the God of the River Arno. H. 90 cm. W. 97,5 cm.
See also A734. Marble versions formerly on the tomb of Philipp Bethmann-Hollweg (1791-1812), now in the Liebighaus in Frankfurt-on Main.

A616 Brother and Sister Leaving their Mother on Earth

Ground floor, northern corridor. Relief. Original plaster model. Rome 1835. H. 96,5 cm. W. 155,5 cm. A marble version executed for the tomb of the children of Princess Helena Poninska in the Palace Chapel in Czerwonogród. Now in the State Museum of Lvov.

A617 Brother and Sister Leaving their Mother on Earth

First floor, room 33. Relief. Preliminary work for A616. Original plaster model. Rome 1834. H. 38,5 cm. W. 59 cm.

A618 Baron Schubart Bids Farewell to his Wife on her Deathbed

Ground floor, northern corridor.
Relief. Original plaster model.
Rome 1814. H. 59 cm. W. 90,7 cm. A marble version A704 was executed for the tomb of Baroness Jacoba Elisabeth Schubart, but never placed.

A619 Count Luigi Porro Lambertenghi and his Children Sorrowing

Ground floor, room 12.
Relief. Original plaster model.
Rome 1817. H. 89,5 cm. W. 91,5 cm. Executed in marble for the tomb of Countess Anna Maria Porro Serbelloni together with reliefs representing Nemesis and the Genius of Death, now in the Galleria d'Arte Moderna, Milan.

A620 Man and Wife Reunited in Heaven

Ground floor, northern corridor.
Relief. Original plaster model.
Rome, c. 1828-30. H. 63,5 cm. W. 56,7 cm. Executed in marble for the tomb of Sir Charles Drake Garrard and wife in the parish church of Wheathampstead, Hertfordshire, England.

A621 Mother Led away from her Son by the Genius of Death

Ground floor, western corridor.
Relief. Original plaster model.
Rome 1816. H. 77,2 cm. W. 101 cm. Executed in marble for the tomb of Countess Jozefa Borkowska in the Dominican Church in Lvov.

A622 The Genius of Death and a Woman Kneeling at a Tombstone

Ground floor, western corridor.
Relief. Plaster cast. The original plaster model A740, Rome 1818. H. 74,5 cm. W. 77 cm. Executed in marble for the tomb of Anthony Radcliffe, Earl of Newburgh, in St. Richard's Church, Slindon, Sussex, England.

A623 Woman Kneeling between Two Angels

Ground floor, northern corridor.
Relief. Original plaster model. Rome 1828. H. 95 cm. W. 128,5 cm. Executed in marble for the tomb of Lady Jane Lawly in the church of Escrick, Yorkshire, England.

A624 Woman Ascending to Heaven, above the Genius of Death

Ground floor, northern corridor.
Relief. Original plaster model.
Rome 1818. H. 122,5 cm. W. 96 cm. Executed in marble for the tomb of Baroness Stanislaus Chaudoir. Present location unknown.

A625 Woman Ascending to Heaven, above the Genius of Death

Ground floor, northern corridor.
Relief, probably a variation of A624. Original plaster model. H. 125 cm. W. 100 cm.

A626 The Genius of Death

First floor, northern corridor.
Relief. Marble version of A627 (Rome 1829). H. 88 cm. W. 77 cm.

A627 The Genius of Death
Ground floor, northern corridor.
Relief. Original plaster model.
Rome 1829. H. 87 cm. W. 73,5
cm. Marble versions A626 and on
the tomb of Count Wlodzimierz
Potocki (see A155) in the Cathedral
on the Wawel in Cracow.

A628 Children Praying
First floor, northern corridor.
Relief. Original plaster model.
Rome 1834. H. 33 cm. W. 47 cm.
Marble version on the tomb of
count Arthur Potocki in the cathedral on the Wawel in Cracow.

A629 Andrea Appiani
First floor, southern corridor.
1754-1817. Italian painter.
Portrait medallion, executed after a
relief by Gaëtano Monti. Original
plaster model. Rome c. 1822. D. 46
cm. A marble version of the medallion placed on the Appiani monument in the Palazzo di Brera, Milan
(see A602).

A630 Ernst Heinrich Løffler
First floor, room 32.
1723-1796. Danish painter and
drawing-master at the Royal Academy of Fine Arts, Copenhagen .
Portrait medallion. Plaster cast. The
original plaster model A864, Copenhagen 1796. D. 46 cm.

A631 Carlo Bassi
First floor, western corridor.
1771-1840. Italian architect. From
1783 settled in Sweden and Finland.
Portrait medallion. Plaster cast. The
original plaster model, Rome 1797.
D. 46,3 cm.

A632 Julius August Walther von Goethe
First floor, northern corridor.
1789-1830. German. Son of
Johann Wolfgang von Goethe.
Portrait medallion. Original plaster
model. Rome 1831. D. 46 cm. Formerly in marble, now in bronze on
the tomb of August von Goethe in
the Protestant Cemetery in Rome.

A633 Henrich Steffens
First floor, western corridor.
1773-1845. Danish philosopher
and naturalist.
Portrait medallion. Original plaster
model. Nysø 1840. D. 46 cm.

A634 Heinrich Reinhold
First floor, room 32.
1788-1825. German painter.
Portrait medallion. Original plaster
model. Rome 1825. D. 46,5 cm.
Formerly in marble, now in bronze
on the tomb of Reinhold in the
Protestant Cemetery in Rome.

A635 Christina Alexandra Egypta Bonaparte?
First floor, southern corridor.
1798-1847. Daughter of Lucien
Bonaparte.
Portrait medallion. Original plaster
model. Rome, probably 1818. D.
46,3 cm. Marble version, see A726.

A636 Thorvaldsen with the Stampe Family
First floor, western corridor.
From left to right: Christian Stampe, Thorvaldsen, Jeanina, Baroness Christine, and Elise Stampe.
On the modelling stand a bozzetto
for the statue of the apostle Andrew
(see A 108).
Relief. Plaster cast. Inscribed: "Nysøe d. 5 Oct 1840". H. 60,3 cm.
W. 99,5 cm.

A637 Baron Stampe and his Sons

First floor, western corridor.
From left to right: Holger, Henrik and Baron Henrik Stampe.
Relief. Plaster cast. The original plaster model, Nysø 1840.
H. 60,3 cm. W. 99,8 cm.

A638-A641

Ground floor, room 19.
A series of reliefs representing the Ages of Man and the Seasons.
Reliefs. Marble versions of A642-A645 (Rome 1836). D. 69 cm.

A638 Childhood - Spring
See above.

A639 Youth - Summer
See above.

A640 Manhood - Autumn
See above.

A641 Old Age - Winter
See above.

A642-A645

First floor, southern corridor.
A series of reliefs representing the Ages of Man and the Seasons.
Reliefs. Original plaster models.
Rome 1836. D. 67,5 cm. Marble versions, see A638-A641.

A642 Childhood - Spring
See above.

A643 Youth - Summer
See above.

A644 Manhood - Autumn
See above.

A645 Old Age- Winter
See above.

A646 Hunter on a Horse

Main staircase.
Relief. Original plaster model.
Rome 1834. H. 105 cm. W. 113,5 cm. Marble version, see A792.

A647 Huntress on a Horse

Main staircase.
Relief. Original plaster model.
Rome 1834. H. 105,5 cm. W. 123 cm. Marble version, see A793.

A648 Bacchante with a Bird

Relief. Original plaster model.
Rome 1837.
H. 49,8 cm. W. 44,3 cm.

A700 Nemesis

Ground floor, room 13.
Tomb for Auguste Böhmer: A700-03.
Relief. Marble version (Thorvaldsen) of A614 completed in 1814.
H. 77,6 cm. W. 45,7 cm.

A701 The Departed Tends her Sick Mother

Ground floor, room 13.
Tomb for Auguste Böhmer: A700-03.
Relief. Marble version (Thorvaldsen) of A614 completed 1814. H. 77,5 cm. W. 63 cm.

A702 The Genius of Death

Ground floor, room 13.
Tomb for Auguste Böhmer: A700-03.
Relief. Marble version (Thorvaldsen) of A614 completed 1814.
H. 77,5 cm. W. 45 cm.

A703 Auguste Böhmer
1785-1800. Daughter of the German physician J. F. N. Böhmer.
Bust. Marble version (Thorvaldsen) executed 1811-1814 after a bust by Chr. Fr. Tieck (G245) intended for the monument for which Thorvaldsen executed the reliefs A700-02.
H. 39 cm.

A704 Baron Herman Schubart Bids Farewell to his Wife on her Deathbed
Ground floor, room 11.
Relief. Tomb for Baroness Jacoba Elisabeth Schubart. Marble version (Thorvaldsen) of A618 (Rome 1814). H. 58,9 cm. W. 93,5 cm.

A705 The Dance of the Muses on Helicon
Apollo, the Muses, and the Graces. Relief. Unfinished. Marble version (Thorvaldsen) of the original plaster model executed in 1804 at Montenero. H. 73 cm. W. 160 cm. See also A340-41.

A706 Stanislaw Kossakowski
1795-1872. Polish count.
Bust. Marble version (Thorvaldsen) of A295 (Rome 1825). H. 57,5 cm.

A707 Griffin and Lyre
Relief, fragment. Probably an original plaster model. Rome c. 1835. H. 64 cm. W. 67,2 cm. Modelled for the base of the Schiller monument (see A135-37 and A770).

A708 Lyre
Relief, fragment. Probably an original plaster model. Rome c. 1835. H. 57,2 cm. W. 35 cm. Modelled for the base of the Schiller monument (see A135-37 and A770).

A709 Base for the Gutenberg Monument with the Relief "The Invention of the Movable Type"
Sketch model. Plaster. Rome c. 1833-34. H. 32. W. 46,9 to 48,5 cm. See A114-15.

A710 Victory Writing on a Shield
Relief. Reworked plaster cast of A361. Rome c. 1830. H. 92,5 cm. W. 71,5 cm.

A711 Coronation Medal with Crown, Sceptre and Sword
Design for the reverse of a medal on the occasion of the coronation of Christian VIII.
Probably an original plaster model. Copenhagen c. 1840. D. 32,2 cm. Attributed to Thorvaldsen.

A712 Alexander the Great in his Triumphal Chariot
Relief. Variation of the central section of A508. Original plaster model. H. 57 cm. W. 101 cm. Marble version, see A509.

A713 Alexander the Great in his Triumphal Chariot
Relief, fragment. Probably an original plaster model for the central section of the Alexander Frieze for Christiansborg Palace. H. 115 cm. W. 105 cm to 81 cm.

A714 Two Men on Horseback in the Train of Alexander the Great

Relief. Section of a recast of A505. Plaster cast. The original plaster model probably executed in Rome 1812. H. 109 cm. W. 152,5 cm. to 164 cm.

A715 Alexander I

1777-1825. Czar of Russia 1801. Bust. Original plaster model. Warsaw 1820. H. 52 cm. Marble version, see A883. See also A246.

A716 Caroline Amalie

1796-1881. Princess, later Queen of Denmark, married to Christian Frederik (Christian VIII) Bust. Original plaster model. Rome 1820-21. H. 39 cm. See also A198 and A754.

A717 George Gordon, Lord Byron

1788-1824, English poet. Bust. Plaster cast; the head of A256. Rome c. 1817. H. 55 cm.

A718 Herman Schubart

1756-1832. Danish baron and diplomat in Italy (Leghorn). Bust. Original plaster model. Montenero 1804. H. 72 cm. Marble version, see A219. See also A812.

A719 Jacoba Elisabeth Schubart

1765-1814. Nee de Wieling, married to Baron Herman Schubart. Bust. Original plaster model. Montenero 1804. H. 58,7 cm. Marble version, see A220. See also A813.

A720 Wilhelmine Benigna Biron

1781-1839. Duchess of Sagan. Bust. Plaster cast before the addition of curls on the forehead and temples. The original plaster model A312, Rome 1818. H. 58,5 cm. See also A811.

A721 François Gabriel de Bray

1765-1832. French by birth, entered Bavarian service as a diplomat. Bavarian Count. Bust. Plaster cast. Inscribed: "A". The original plaster model A300, Rome c. 1818-19. H. 51,5 cm.

A722 Leonardo Pisano, Fibonacci

C. 1170 - c. 1240. Italian mathematician. Bust. Original plaster model. Rome between 1834 and 1838. H. 73 cm. Marble version, see A187.

A723 Head of a Woman with Tiara

Head executed for the restoration of an antique bronze statue in the Glyptothek, Munich, the so-called "Spinnerin". Original plaster model. Rome 1837. H. 37,5 cm.

A724 Andreas Peter Bernstorff

1735-1797. Danish statesman and count. Mask. Plaster cast of A856. Inscribed: "A. P. Bernstorff afst. af buste". The original plaster model, Copenhagen 1795. H. 23,6 cm.

A725 Karl Philipp von Schwarzenberg
1771-1820. Austrian prince and general, Duke of Krumau. Mask. Plastercast, probably of an earlier version of the bust A236. Rome 1821. H 26 cm.

A726 Christina Alexandra Egypta Bonaparte?
1798-1847. Daughter of Lucien Bonaparte. Portrait medallion. Marble version of A635 (Rome, probably 1818). D. 49 cm.

A727 Marianna Florenzi
Ground floor, southern corridor.
1802-1870. Née Baccinetti, married to Marchese Ettore Florenzi. Bust. Marble version of A278 (Rome 1828), begun by Thorvaldsen in 1829 in Rome, and completed in 1858 in Copenhagen under the supervision of H. W. Bissen. H. 74,4 cm.

A728 Pan and Hunting Nymph
First floor, southern corridor.
Relief. Marble version of A356 (Rome c. 1838). H 69,7 cm. W. 60, 7 cm.

A729 Cupid and the Tamed Lion
First floor, southern corridor.
Relief. Marble version of A387 (Rome 1828). H. 49 cm. W. 65,5 cm.

A730 The Baptism of Christ
Relief. Plaster cast. The original plaster model, Copenhagen 1820. H. 95 cm. W. 223,5 cm. See also A557.

A731 Hymen
Relief. Probably an original plaster model. D. 94 cm.

A732 Napoleon I
1769-1821. Emperor of France 1804-14. Bust. Marble version of A909 (Rome c. 1830), begun in Rome and completed in Copenhagen under the supervision of H. W. Bissen. H. 99,9 cm. See also A252 and A867.

A733 Ganymede with Jupiter's Eagle
Statue. Plaster cast of a reduced version of A44. H. 37 cm. to 46,5 cm. W. 59,5 cm.

A734 Woman Sorrowing
Relief, fragment from the tomb of Philipp Bethmann-Hollweg. Plaster cast. The original plaster model, Rome 1814. H. 88,5 cm. W. 33 cm to 29 cm. See also A615.

A735 Chimney-Piece with Two Caryatids and a Frieze of Cupids.
Relief. Marble. Rome, early 1820(?). H. 135,5 cm. W. 201,5 cm. See A56 and A592.

A736 The Baptism of Christ
Relief. Probably an original plaster model executed for the Brahetrolleborg Baptismal Font (1805-07). H. 82 cm. W. 54 cm. to 63 cm. See A555.

A737 Christ Blessing the Children
Relief. Probably an original plaster model executed for the Brahetrolleborg Baptismal Font (1805-07). H. 71 cm. W. 54 cm. See A555.

A738 Thorvaldsen, Sommariva and a Greek Warrior
Relief. Original plaster model. Rome c. 1825. H. 103 cm. W. 136 cm. to 129 cm. The end-piece of the Alexander Frieze executed for Count G. B. Sommariva. See A505.

A739 The Ages of Love
Relief. An adaptation of A427. Probably an original plaster model. Copenhagen 1843. H. 50,5 cm. W. 144 cm. See also A426.

A740 The Genius of Death and a Woman Kneeling at a Tombstone
Relief. Original plaster model. Rome 1818. H. 76 cm. W. 81 cm. Executed in marble for the tomb of Anthony Radcliffe, Earl of Newburgh, in St. Richard's Church, Slindon, Sussex, England. See also A622.

A741 Giovanni-Battista Sommariva
C. 1750-1826. Italian count, politician, and art collector. Bust. Marble version of A273 (Rome 1817 or 1818). H. 51,7 cm. See also A272.

A742 Perseus on Pegasus Rescuing Andromeda
Relief. Original plaster model. Nysø 1839. D. 77 cm.

A743 Andreas Peter Bernstorff
1735-1797. Danish statesman and count. Portrait medallion. Plaster cast. Inscribed: "B. Thorvaldsen F. 1796". The original plaster model A817, Copenhagen 1796. D. 35,7 cm.

A744 Peter Johan Monrad
1758-1834. Danish high-ranking civil servant. Portrait medallion. Probably a plaster cast, painted. Copenhagen before 1796. D. 42 cm.

A745 Cecilia Kirstine Monrad
1761-1839. Married to Peter Johan Monrad. Portrait medallion. Probably a plaster cast, painted. Copenhagen, before 1796. D. 41,5 cm.

A746 Peter Johan Monrad.
1758-1834. Danish high-ranking civil servant. Portrait medallion. Probably a plaster cast, painted. Copenhagen before 1796. D. 42 cm.

A747 Cecilia Kirstine Monrad
1761-1839. Married to Peter Johan Monrad. Portrait medallion. Probably a plaster cast, painted. Copenhagen before 1796. D. 42 cm.

A748 King Numa Pompilius Conversing with the Nymph Egeria in her Grotto
Relief. Plaster cast. Inscribed: "B. Thorvaldsen: Fec. 1794". Copenhagen. H. 48 cm. W. 61 cm.

A749 Hercules and Omphale
Relief. Plaster cast. Copenhagen 1792. H. 48 cm. W. 60 cm.

A750 Mother and Two Children
Statuette. Original plaster model. Copenhagen c. 1793. H. 38,5 cm. Purchased in 1850 at an auction over the estate of the widow of the Danish painter N. A. Abildgaard.

A751 Homer

7th century B. C. Greek poet. Bust. Marble version (Thorvaldsen). Rome 1799. Copy of an antique bust. H. 51,4 cm. Purchased 1850 at an auction over the estate of the widow of the Danish painter N. A. Abildgaard.

A752 Raphael

1483-1520. Italian artist. Bust. Marble version (Thorvaldsen). Rome 1800. Copy of a bust of Raphael by Pietro Paolo Naldini, placed 1674 in the Pantheon in Rome and moved in 1820 to La Protomoteca on the Capitoline Hill. H. 54 cm. Purchased in 1850 at an auction over the estate of the widow of the Danish painter N. A. Abildgaard.

A753 Christian Frederik

Ground floor, room 20.

1786-1848. Danish prince, from 1839 King Christian VIII of Denmark. Bust. Original plaster model. Rome 1821. H. 69 cm. See also A197.

A754 Caroline Amalie

1796-1881. Princess, later Queen of Danmark, married to Christian Frederik (Christian VIII). Bust. Plaster cast. The original plaster model A716, Rome 1820-21. H. 67 cm. See also A198.

A755 Shepherd Boy

Sketch model for A177. Plaster. Rome 1817. H. 52,5 cm. Purchased 1854 from the Buti family in Rome. Thorvaldsen lived in the Casa Buti in the Via Sistina.

A756 Cupid Resting

Oval relief. Original plaster model. Inscribed: "Thorvaldsen fec." Copenhagen 1789. H. 76,5 cm. W. 56 cm. Awarded the Major Silver Medal of the Academy of Fine Arts, Copenhagen. Presented by the Academy in 1855.

A757 The Muse Euterpe

Statuette. Original plaster model, painted. Copenhagen 1794. H. 49,2 cm. Sketch model for a statue in Prince Frederik's (later Christian X's) palace at Amalienborg, from a composition by N. A. Abildgaard. Presented by the Academy of Fine Arts in 1855.

A758 The Muse Terpsichore

Statuette. Original plaster model, painted. Copenhagen 1794. H. 49,5 cm. Sketch model for a statue in Prince Frederik's (later Christian X's) palace at Amalienborg, from a composition by N. A. Abildgaard. Presented by the Academy of Fine Arts 1855.

A759 Agrippa 63 B. C. - 12 B. C. Roman consul and commander.

Bust. Marble version (Thorvaldsen). Rome 1799-1800. Copy of an antique bust. H. 50,5 cm. Presented by the Academy of Fine Arts in 1855.

A760 Cicero

106 B. C. - 43 B. C. Roman statesman and orator. Bust. Marble version (Thorvaldsen). Rome 1799-1800. Copy of an antique bust. H. 43 cm. Presented by the Academy of Fine Arts in 1855.

A761 Cicero
106 B. C. - 43 B. C. Roman statesman and orator.
Bust. Marble version (Thorvaldsen). Rome 1799-1800. Copy of an antique bust. H. 48,5 cm. Presented by the Academy of Fine Arts in 1855.

A762 Maximilian I
See A128

A763 Sophie Dorothea Høyer
C. 1743-1808. Nee Heldvad, married to Pastor Jens Offesen Høyer. The mother of the painter Christian Fœdder Høyer.
Bust. Marble version (Thorvaldsen) of A228 (Rome 1809). H. 39,6 cm. Bequeathed by C. F. Høyer in 1855.

A764 Simon Jensen
1749-1800. Danish bookkeeper, administrator of The Danish West India Trading Company.
Portrait medallion. Original plaster model, painted. Inscribed: "B. Thorvaldsen Fec 1793".Copenhagen. D. 42 cm. Presented by C. J. Glahn in 1856.

A765 Eleonora Maria Jensen
Née Weygaard, married to Simon Jensen.
Portrait medallion. Original plaster model, painted. Inscribed: "B. Thorvaldsen Fec 1793". Copenhagen. D. 42 cm. Presented by C. J. Glahn in 1856.

A766 The Children of Simon Jensen
Left: Anna Birgitte Margrethe (1784-1823), later married to pharmacist Hans Egede Glahn. Right: Johan Otto Jensen (1786-1809). Portrait medallion. Original plaster model, painted. Inscribed: "B. Thorvaldsen Fec 1793". Copenhagen. D. 41 cm. Presented by C. J. Glahn, in 1856.

A767 Simon Jensen
1749-1800. Danish bookkeeper, administrator of The Danish West India Trading Company.
Portrait medallion. Plaster cast of the original plaster model A764, Copenhagen 1793. D. 42 cm.

A768 Eleonora Maria Jensen
Nee Weygaard, married to Simon Jensen.
Portrait medallion. Plaster cast of the original plaster model A765, Copenhagen 1793. D. 42 cm.

A769 The Children of Simon Jensen
Left: Anna Birgitte Margrethe (1784-1823), later married to pharmacist Hans Egede Glahn. Right: Johan Otto Jensen (1786-1809). Portrait medallion. Plaster cast of the original plaster model A766, Copenhagen 1793. D. 41 cm.

A770 Friedrich Schiller
Entrance hall.
1759-1805. German poet. Statue. Original plaster model. Rome 1836. H. 391 cm. Modelled by W. Matthiä after Thorvaldsen's sketch model (see A138). Erected in bronze in Stuttgart in 1839. Purchased in 1857 fom the Württembergische Kunstschule, Stuttgart.

A771 Bertel Thorvaldsen Leaning on the Statue of Hope
Ground floor, room 20.
1770-1844. Self-portrait.
Statue. Marble version executed in 1859 for the Museum by H. W. Bissen. The original plaster model, Nysø 1839. H. 198 cm. See also A162.

A772 The Hours
Relief. Plaster cast. The original plaster model Dep. 22 executed in 1794 in Copenhagen for Prince Frederik's (later Christian X's) palace at Amalienborg, from a composition by N. A. Abildgaard. H. 57 cm. W. 94 cm. Presented by the restorer P. H. Rasmussen in 1865.

A773 Georgiana Elizabeth Russell
First floor, room 25.
C. 1810-1867. Daughter of John Russell, Duke of Bedford.
Statue. Marble version of A173 executed in 1866 by Christian Freund under the supervision of H. W. Bissen. The original plaster model, Rome 1815. H 101,2 cm.

A774 Hector with Paris and Helen
Ground floor, room 7.
Relief. Marble version of A499 (Rome 1809) executed 1868 for the Museum by Christian Freund under the supervision of H. W. Bissen. H. 72 cm. W. 94 cm.

A775 Priam Pleads with Achilles for Hector's Body
Ground floor, room 5.
Relief. Marble version of A492 (Rome 1815) executed in 1868-70 for the Museum by Christian Freund under the supervision of H. W. Bissen. H. 96 cm. W. 198,5 cm.

A776 Hector's Farewell to Andromache
Ground floor, room 7.
Relief. Marble version of A501 (Rome 1837) executed in 1867-70 by H. W. and V. Bissen. H. 93,5 cm. W. 184,2 cm. Presented by the brewer J. C. Jacobsen in 1870.

A777 Achilles and Penthesilea
Statuette. Original plaster model. Rome 1801. H. 65,5 cm. Bequeathed by J. M. Thiele in 1875.

A778 Dancing Girl
Sketch model for A178. Plaster. Rome, probably 1817. H. 54,5 cm. Purchased 1875.

A779 Actaeon Torn by his Dogs
First floor, room 22.
Oval relief. Plaster cast. H. 33,5 cm. W. 25 cm. See A461. Presented by the sculptor C. Freund in 1875.

A780 Cupid Stung by a Bee Complains to Venus
First floor, northern corridor.
Relief. Original plaster model. Rome 1809. H. 46 cm. W. 51,5 cm. Marble version, see A417. Presented by the sculptor C. Freund in 1876.

A781 Angel Kneeling with a Baptismal Font
Bozzetto for A112. Terracotta. Rome, probably 1823. H. 30,7 cm. Bequeathed by Consul Johan Bravo 1876.

A782 Bernt Anker?
1746-1805. Norwegian owner of ironworks.
Portrait medallion. Terracotta. Copenhagen c. 1796. D. 21,5 cm. Purchased 1879.

A783 Minerva
First floor, room 22.
Bozzetto. Terracotta. Fragment of the clay model for A17 (Copenhagen 1843). H. 7,7 cm. W. 5,5 cm. Purchased 1879.

A784 Aesculapius
Bozzetto. Terracotta. Fragment of the clay model for A20 (Copenhagen 1843). H. 10,5 cm. W. 6,3 cm. Purchased 1879.

A785 Genius
Bozzetto. Terracotta. Fragment of the clay model for A607. Inscribed: "6 Mai 1843". Copenhagen. H. 7 cm. W. 5,5 cm. Purchased 1879.

A786 Cupid Playing a Lyre
First floor, northern corridor.
Statue. Original plaster model. Rome 1819. H. 60 cm. Marble version, see A33. Purchased 1882.

A787 The Royal Coat of Arms
Relief. Painted sandstone. Copenhagen 1789. H. 70 cm. W. 205 cm. Executed for the Court Pharmacy, formerly at 25 Store Kongensgade, Copenhagen. Presented by Mr. Ibsen, Court Pharmacist, in 1882.

A788 Christoffer Wilhelm Eckersberg
Ground floor, room 1.
1783-1853. Danish painter.
Bust. Marble version (Thorvaldsen) of A224 (Rome 1816). Inscribed: "ECKERSBERG PITTORE/THORVALD-

SEN •FACEVA ROMA•LI•XII• MAGGIO•MDCCCXVI". H. 53,5 cm. Presented by C. W. Eckersberg's daughters in 1883.

A789 Adonis
Statue. Plaster cast of the marble version in Munich. The original plaster model A53, Rome 1808. H. 185 cm. Purchased 1886.

A790 Adonis
Ground floor, room 17.
Statue. Marble version of A53 (Rome 1808) and A789 executed in 1887 for the Museum by A. Saabye. H. 186 cm.

A791 Achilles and Priam
Relief. Original plaster model. Copenhagen 1791. H. 67 cm. W. 78,5 cm. Presented by the Academy of Fine Arts in 1887.

A792 Hunter on a Horse
Ground floor, room 17.
Relief. Marble version of A646 (Rome 1834) executed in 1886-87 for the Museum by C. Aarsleff under the supervision of C. Peters. H. 103 cm. W. 114 cm.

A793 Huntress on a Horse
Ground floor, room 17.
Relief. Marble version of A647 (Rome 1834) executed in 1886-87 for the Museum by C. Aarsleff under the supervision of C. Peters. H. 102 cm. W. 123,3 cm.

A794 Wlodzimierz Potocki
Ground floor, room 15.
1789-1812. Polish count and general.
Statue. Marble version of A155 (Rome 1821) executed in 1886-88 for the Museum by V. Bissen. H. 215,3 cm.

A795 Jon Erichsen
1728-1787. Born in Iceland, lawyer and philologist.
Mask. Plaster. H. 20 cm. Probably a cast of a fragment of the Erichsen bust which was executed in plaster in Copenhagen in 1794 and broke during its transportation from Copenhagen to Iceland in 1825. See also A862. Purchased 1888.

A796 Mercury Brings the Infant Bacchus to Ino
Ground floor, room 14.
Relief. Marble version of A347 (Rome 1809) executed in 1889 for the Museum by R. Andersen under the supervision of T. Stein. H. 48,5 cm. W. 49 cm.

A797 Cupid and Bacchus
Ground floor, room 4.
Relief. Marble version of the original plaster model (Rome 1810?) in the Museum of Fine Arts in Randers executed in 1889 for the Museum by R. Andersen under the supervision of T. Stein. H. 53 cm. W. 72,3 cm.

A798 The Centaur Chiron Teaching Achilles to Throw a Spear
Ground floor, room 17.
Relief. Marble version of A488 (Rome 1837) executed in 1888-90 for the Museum by R. Andersen under the supervision of T. Stein. H. 101,5 cm. W. 123,5 cm.

A802 Jacob Baden
1735-1804. Danish author and philologist.
Bust. Original plaster model. Inscribed: "B. Thorvaldsen f.". Rome

1806. H. 33,3 cm. Formerly believed to represent the Danish archaeologist Georg Zoega. Marble version, see A803. See also A863. Purchased 1898.

A803 Jacob Baden
1735-1804. Danish author and philologist.
Bust. Marble version of A802 (Rome 1806) executed by T. Stein. Inscribed: "1755 G. Zoega. 1809" and on the back: "B. Thorvaldsen Rom". H. 31 cm. See also A863. Purchased 1898.

A804 Cupid Triumphant
Ground floor, room 16.
Statue. Marble version of A22 executed in 1897-99 for the Museum by R. Andersen under the supervision of T. Stein. The original plaster model, Rome 1814. H. 144 cm.

A805 Cupid's Torso
Relief. Terracotta. Fragment of the clay model for A450 (Nysø 1840). Inscribed: "Af A. Thorvaldsens egenhœndige Modellering paa Nysø 1841-44." H. 16,5 cm. Purchased 1900.

A806 Cupid's Head
Relief. Terracotta. Fragment of the clay model for A450 (Nysø 1840). Inscribed: "Af A. Thorvaldsens egenhœndige Modellering paa Nysø 1841-44." H. 7,5 cm. Purchased 1900.

A807 Cupid's Wing
Relief. Terracotta. Fragment of the clay model for A450 (Nysø 1840). Inscribed: "A. Thorvaldsens originale Arbejde paa Nysø 1841-44." H. 14,5 cm. Purchased 1900.

A808 Psyche's Head

Relief. Terracotta. Fragment of the clay model for A450 (Nysø 1840). Inscribed: "A. Thorvaldsens egenhœndige Modellering paa Nysø 1841-44". H. 10 cm. Purchased 1900.

A809 Fragment of a Leg

Relief. Terracotta. Fragment of the clay model for A604 (Copenhagen 1842). Inscribed: "Af A. Thorvaldsens originale Arbejde paa Nysø 1841-44". H. 10,3 cm. Purchased 1900.

A810 Ida Brun

Ground floor, room 17.
1792-1857. Daughter of Constantin and Friederike Brun. Married Count Louis Philippe Bombelles, Austrian diplomat.
Bust. Marble version (Thorvaldsen) of A218 (Rome 1809). H. 56,5 cm. Bequeathed by Fritz Brun, Royal Chamberlain, 1902.

A811 Wilhelmine Benigna Biron

First floor, landing.
1781-1839. Duchess of Sagan. Bust. Plaster cast before the addition of curls on the forehead and temples. The original plaster model A312, Rome 1818. H. 58 cm. See also A720. Presented in 1909 by Baron August Binzer, Munich.

A812 Herman Schubart

1756-1832. Danish baron and diplomat in Italy (Leghorn). Bust. Plaster cast of A219. The original plaster model A718, Montenero 1804. H. 70,4 cm. Presented by the Academy of Fine Arts in 1910.

A813 Jacoba Elisabeth Schubart

1765-1814. Née de Wieling. Married to Baron Herman Schubart. Bust. Plaster cast of A220. The original plaster model A719, Montenero 1804. H. 70,4 cm. Presented by the Academy of Fine Arts in 1910.

A814 Head of a Bacchante

Relief. Terracotta. Fragment of the clay model for A358 (Nysø 1840-41). Inscribed: "Af A. Thorvaldsens egenhændige Modellering paa Nysø 1841-44". H. 8 cm. Purchased 1910.

A815 Michael Rosing

1756-1818. Danish actor. Portrait medallion. Plaster, painted. Inscribed: "B. Thorvaldsen fec. 1793". Copenhagen. D. 42 cm. Purchased 1910.

A816 Johanne Cathrine Rosing

1756-1853. Danish actress, nee Olsen. Portrait medallion Plaster, painted. Inscribed: "B. Thorvaldsen Fec (1793?)". Copenhagen. D. 42 cm. Purchased 1910.

A817 Andreas Peter Bernstorff

1735-1797. Danish statesman and count. Portrait medallion. Original plaster model, painted and gilded. Inscribed: "B. Thorvaldsen født [sic] 1796" Copenhagen. D. 40 cm. Purchased 1911.

A818 Louise Augusta

1771-1843. Danish princess, married to Count Frederik Christian of Augustenborg.
Portrait medallion. Original plaster model, painted and gilded. Inscribed: "Thorvaldsen Fec 1793". Copenhagen. D. 42 cm. Purchased 1911.

A819 Cupid Standing with his Bow

First floor, room 29.
Statue. Marble version of A36 (Rome, probably 1819). Inscribed: "Thorvaldsen. F." H. 101 cm. Purchased 1914.

A820 Conradin

1252-1268. The last of the Hohenstaufens.
Sketch model. Plaster cast of A151 (Rome 1833). H. 52 cm. Presented by the Ny Carlsberg Glyptotek, Copenhagen, 1915.

A821 Psyche with the Jar of Beauty

Statue. Marble version (Thorvaldsen) of A26 (Rome 1806). H. 132 cm. Purchased at the Hope Auction, "The Deepdene", Surrey, England in 1917.

A822 Jason with the Golden Fleece

Ground floor, room 5.
Statue. Marble version (Thorvaldsen) of A52 (Rome 1802-03). Inscribed: "A". Commissioned by Thomas Hope 1803, completed in 1828 in Rome. H. 242 cm. Purchased at the Hope Auction, "The Deepdene", Surrey, England in 1917.

A823 Thomas Hope

Ground floor, room 5.
1769-1831. English art collector and author.
Bust. Marble version (Thorvaldsen) of A298 (Rome 1817). H 55,4 cm. Purchased at the Hope Auction, "The Deepdene", Surrey, England in 1917.

A824 Louisa Hope

Ground floor, room 5.
C. 1786-1851. Née de la Poer Beresford, married to Thomas Hope.
Bust. Marble version (Thorvaldsen) of A264 (Rome 1817) . H. 58,5 cm. Purchased at the Hope Auction, "The Deepdene", Surrey, England in 1917.

A825 Henry Thomas Hope

Ground floor, room 6.
1808-1862. Son of Thomas and Louisa Hope.
Bust. Marble version (Thorvaldsen) of A265 (Rome c. 1822-23). H. 47,2 cm. Purchased at the Hope Auction "The Deepdene", Surrey, England in 1917.

A826 Adrian John Hope

Ground floor, room 6.
1811-1863. Son of Thomas and Louisa Hope.
Bust. Marble version (Thorvaldsen) of the original plaster model executed c. 1817 in Rome. H. 41,5 cm. Purchased at the Hope Auction, "The Deepdene", Surrey, England 1917.

A827 Cupid Received by Anacreon

Ground floor, room 4.
Relief. Marble version (Thorvaldsen) of the original plaster model executed in 1823 in Rome. From Anacreontea, Song 3, which also inspired H. C. Andersen to write the story of "The Mischievous Boy". Presented by Thorvaldsen to Thomas Hope in 1828. H 48,5 cm. W. 70 cm. See also A415. Purchased at the Hope Auction, "The Deepdene", Surrey, England 1917.

A828 Art and the Lightbringing Genius, A Genio Lumen.

Ground floor, room 20.
Relief. Marble version (Thorvaldsen) of A518 (Rome 1808). Presented by Thorvaldsen to Thomas Hope 1828. H. 99,5 cm. W. 131,5 cm. Purchased at the Hope Auction, "The Deepdene", Surrey, England 1917.

A829 Heliodorus Driven out of the Temple

Relief. Original plaster model. Copenhagen 1791. Awarded the Minor Gold Medal of the Royal Academy of Fine Arts, Copenhagen. H. 114 cm. W. 173 cm. Presented by the Academy of Fine Arts in 1918. A830 The Apostles Peter and John Healing a Lame Man before the Gate of the Temple.

A830 The Apostles Peter and John Healing a Lame Man before the Gate of the Temple.

Basement, room 63.
Relief. Original plaster model. Co-

penhagen 1793. Awarded the Major Gold Medal of the Academy of Fine Arts, Copenhagen. H. 117,5 cm. W. 173,5 cm. Presented by the Academy of Fine Arts in 1918.

A831-A850 Fragments of the Alexander Frieze

20 relief fragments from the Alexander Frieze executed for Christiansborg Palace. Marble. Commissioned in 1818 and partly destroyed by fire in 1884. See A503. Presented by the Ministry of Internal Affairs in 1919.

A851 Christian August Tiedge

Ground floor, northern corridor.
1752-1841. German poet.
Bust. Marble version (Thorvaldsen) of A240 (Rome c. 1805-06). H. 60,5 cm. Purchased 1920.

A852 Elisabeth (Elisa) von der Recke

Ground floor, northern corridor.
1754-1833. German countess and poetess, née von Medem.
Bust. Marble version (Thorvaldsen) of the original plaster model executed 1805-06 in Rome. H. 69,3 cm. See also A869 and A879. Purchased 1920.

A853 Venus with the Apple Awarded by Paris

Ground floor, room 4.
Statue. Marble version (Thorvaldsen) of A12 (Rome 1813-16), probably executed for P. C. Labouchére. Inscribed: "Thorwaldsen. F." H. 160,8 cm. Purchased 1920.

A854 Ganymede Offering the Cup
Ground floor, room 1.
Statue. Marble version (Thorvaldsen) of the original plaster model executed in 1804 in Rome. Inscribed: "AT". H. 136,5 cm. See also A41. Purchased 1920.

A855 Christmas Joy in Heaven
Basement, room 45.
Relief. Marble version (Thorvaldsen), unfinished. The original plaster model, Nysø 1842. D. 101 cm. See also A589. Entered in the inventory in 1921.

A856 Andreas Peter Bernstorff
1735-1797. Danish statesman and count.
Bust. Old plaster cast. Inscribed: "B. Thorvaldsen Fec 179(5)." Copenhagen. H. 80,8 cm. See also A208. Presented by the Ministry of Internal Affairs in 1922.

A857 Caroline
Ground floor, room 18.
1793-1881. Danish princess, daughter of Frederik VI.
Bust. Marble version (Thorvaldsen) of A193 (Copenhagen 1819-20). Inscribed: "Thorvaldsen F". H. 69 cm. Purchased 1922.

A858 Nicolaus Copernicus
1473-1543. Astronomer.
Sketch model for A113. Plaster. Rome 1821. H. 46 cm. Presented by shipowner Marius Nielsen in 1922.

A859 Frederik VI
Ground floor, room 18.
1768-1839. King of Denmark from 1808.

Bust. Marble version (Thorvaldsen) of the original plaster model executed 1819-20 in Copenhagen. Inscribed: "Thorvaldsen F". H. 69,3 cm. See also A191. Purchased 1923.

A860 Marie Sophie Frederikke
Ground floor, room 18.
1767-1852. Queen of Denmark, married to Frederik VI.
Bust. Marble version (Thorvaldsen) of A192 (Copenhagen 1819-20). Inscribed: "Thorvaldsen F". H. 72,8 cm. Purchased 1923.

A861 Karoline von Rehfues
Ground floor, room 17.
1799-1892. Née von Meusebach, married to the German author Philipp Joseph von Rehfues.
Bust. Marble version (Thorvaldsen) of A245 (Rome 1827). H. 54,7 cm. Purchased 1923.

A862 Jon Erichsen
1728-1787. Born in Iceland, lawyer and philologist.
Mask. Plaster. H. 20 cm. Probably a cast of a fragment of the Erichsen bust which was executed in plaster in Copenhagen in 1794 and broke during its transportation from Copenhagen to Iceland in 1825. See also A795. Purchased 1923.

A863 Jacob Baden
1735-1804. Danish author and philologist.
Bust. Marble version (Thorvaldsen) of the original plaster model executed 1806 in Rome after a death mask and a painted portrait. H. 54,8 cm. See also A802 and A803. Purchased 1924.

A864 Ernst Heinrich Løffler

1723-1796. Danish painter and drawing-master at the Royal Academy of Fine Arts, Copenhagen. Portrait medallion. Original plaster model. Copenhagen 1796. D. 57 cm. See also A630. Presented by the sculptor E. Utzon-Frank in 1926.

A866 Cupid Revives the Swooning Psyche

Ground floor, room 2.
Relief. Marble version (Thorvaldsen) of A431 (Montenero 1810). H. 49,5 cm. W. 78 cm. See also A430. Purchased 1926.

A867 Napoleon I

1769-1821. Emperor of France 1804-14. Bust. Marble version (Thorvaldsen) of A909 (Rome c. 1830). H. 99,9 cm. See also A252 and A732. Purchased 1929.

A868 Mercury about to Kill Argus

Sketch model for A5. Plaster. Rome 1818. H. 52,2 cm. Formerly in the collection of the composer F. Mendelssohn-Bartholdy. Purchased 1931.

A869 Elisabeth (Elisa) von der Recke

1754-1833. German countess and poetess, nee von Medem. Bust. Marble version (Thorvaldsen) of A879 (Rome 1805-06). H. 41,8 cm. See also A852. Purchased 1931.

A870 Hebe

First floor, southern corridor.
Statue. An adaptation of A37, probably an original plaster model. Rome 1816. H. 155 cm. Marble version, see A874. See also A39. Purchased 1934.

A871 Charlotte Dorothea Fischer

1784-1855. Nee Schweffel, married to the Danish officer Frederik Fischer. Portrait medallion. Plaster cast. The original plaster model, Rome, between 1833 and 1837. D. 31,5 cm. Purchased 1934.

A872 Man on Horseback

Relief. Decoration above a gateway, carved in wood by Thorvaldsen in 1792 in Copenhagen after a drawing by the Navy sculptor F. C. Willerup for 17 Ny Vestergade. H. 123 cm. W. 137,2 cm. Presented by Den sjællandske Bondestands Sparekasse in 1936.

A873 Mercury about to Kill Argus

Ground floor, room 10.
Statue. Marble version (Thorvaldsen) of A5 (Rome 1818). Inscribed: "A. Thorwaldsen fecit". H. 174,5 cm. Purchased from Lord Ashburton, "The Grange", Hampshire in 1938.

A874 Hebe

Ground floor, room 6.
Statue. Marble version (Thorvaldsen) of A870 (Rome 1816). Inscribed: "A Thorwaldsen fecit". H. 152,2 cm. See also A39. Purchased from Lord Ashburton, "The Grange", Hampshire, in 1938.

A875 Hebe

Statue. Marble version (Thorvaldsen) of A37 (Rome 1806). Inscribed: "AT". H. 156,5 cm. Purchased from William Randolph Hearst's collection in 1938.

A876 Ludvig Holberg
First floor, northern corridor.
1684-1754. Danish playwright,
historian, and philosopher. Bust.
Original plaster model. Nysø and
Copenhagen 1839. H. 54,7 cm.
See also A190. Entered in the
inventory in 1938.

A877 Rosa Taddei
1799-1869. Italian improvisatrice.
Bust. Original plaster model. Rome
1826. H. 50,5 cm. Entered in the
inventory in 1941.

A878 Cupid Asks Jupiter and Juno that the Rose May Be Queen of Flowers.
Relief. Plaster cast, probably of the
sketch model for A394. H. 17 cm.
W. 27 cm. Purchased 1941.

A879 Elisabeth (Elisa) von der Recke
1754-1833. German countess and
poetess, née von Medem.
Bust. Original plaster model. Rome,
probably 1805-06. H. 38,2 cm.
Marble version, see A869. See also
A852. Purchased 1944.

A880 Bertel Thorvaldsen's Head
Bozzetto. Terracotta. Fragment of
the clay model for the self-portrait
statue. H. 9 cm. See A163.
Purchased 1944.

A881 Jacob Laurids Thrane
1785-1819. Danish architect.
Bust. Original plaster model. Rome
c. 1806. H. 52,8 cm. Marble version, see Dep. 36. Entered in the
inventory in 1946.

A882 Christ
Mask. Plaster cast of the face of the
marble version of the Christ statue
in The Church of Our Lady, Copenhagen. H. 44,5 cm. See A82.
Entered in the inventory in 1946.

A883 Alexander I
Ground floor, room 12.
1777-1825. Czar of Russia 1801.
Bust. Marble version (Thorvaldsen)
of A715 (Warsaw 1820). Inscribed:
"A . Thorvaldsen F. 1821.".
H. 67, 8 cm. Purchased 1946.

A884 Horace Vernet
1789-1863. French painter.
Bust. Plaster cast, probably of the
original plaster model A254, Rome
1832. H. 48,5 cm. Entered in the
inventory in 1946.

A885 Jacob Loewy?
Died c. 1830. Austrian philanthro-
pist.
Bust. Plaster cast. The original plas-
ter model, Rome 1831. H. 51,6 cm.
Entered in the inventory in 1946.

A886 Vittoria Caldoni
Basement, room 46.
1807-?. Italian model from Albano.
Bust. Marble version (Thorvaldsen)
of A279 (Rome 1821). H. 52 cm.
Formerly in the collection of P. O.
Brøndsted. Purchased 1947.

A887 Ghazi 'L-Din Haidar
Ground floor, room 11.
Padishah of Oudh, King of Oudh
1819-27.
Bust. Marble version (Thorvaldsen)
of A280 (Rome 1824). Inscribed:
"A. Thorvaldsen f. 1824". H. 81,9
cm. Purchased 1949.

A888 Unknown Lady

Portrait medallion. Original plaster model. Probably Copenhagen c. 1796. D. 45 cm. The attribution to Thorvaldsen unsure. Entered in the inventory in 1950.

A889 Anne, Countess of Newburgh

C. 1762-1861. Née Webb, married to A .J. Radcliffe, Earl of Newburgh. Oval portrait medallion. Original plaster model. Rome, probably 1818. H. 31,3 cm. W. 30,2 cm. Entered in the inventory in 1950.

A890 Georg Wilhelm Wilding

Ground floor, northern corridor.
1790-1841. Married to Donna Catharina de Branciforte, became the Principe di Butera in 1814 after the death of his father-in-law. Bust. Marble version (Thorvaldsen) of A275 (Rome 1815). Inscribed: "AT". H. 68,5 cm. Purchased 1950.

A891 Catharina de Branciforte

Ground floor, northern corridor.
1768-1824. Née Branciforte e Pignatelli, daughter of the Principe de Butera. Married in 1812 to Georg Wilhelm Wilding. 1814 Principessa di Butera. Bust. Marble version (Thorvaldsen) of A276 (Rome 1815). Inscribed: "AT". H. 70,5 cm. Purchased 1950.

A892 George Hilaro Barlow

Ground floor, room 12.
1762-1848. Knighted 1803. Governor General of India 1805-07. Governor of Madras 1807-12.

Bust. Marble version (Thorvaldsen) of A289 (Rome 1828). Inscribed: "Thorvaldsen. F." and "S. G. H. Barlow". H. 64 cm. Presented in 1950 by Victoria, Lady Barlow, England.

A893 Thomson Henry Bonar

Ground floor, room 11.
C. 1810-1817. Son of Colonel Thomson Bonar. Bust. Marble version (Thorvaldsen) of the original plaster model executed in 1817 in Rome. Inscribed: "Thorvaldsen. Faciebat. Romae. MDCCCXVII. Thomson. Hen. Bonar/OB. Romae. Vix. Ann. VII." H. 56,2 cm. Purchased 1950.

A894 Cupid and the Graces

Ground floor, room 3.
Statue. Marble version (Thorvaldsen) of A29 (Rome 1817-19). Inscribed: "Thorvaldsen Fecit". H. 172,7 cm. Purchased 1952.

A895 Shepherd Boy

Ground floor, room 19.
Statue. Marble version (Thorvaldsen) of A177 (Rome 1817), probably executed 1822-5. Inscribed: "A. Thorvaldsen Fecit". H. 148 cm. Purchased 1952.

A896 Holger Christian Reiersen

1746-1811. Danish Titular Councillor of State.
Portrait medallion. Original plaster model (?), bronzed. Inscribed: "B. Thorvald(sen) Fec 1793". Copenhagen. D. 24 cm. Purchased 1953.

A897 Charlotte Kirstine Reiersen

1763-1810. Née Studsgaard, married to H. C. Reiersen.
Portrait medallion. Original plaster model (?), bronzed. Inscribed: "B. Thorvald(sen) Fec 1793". Copenhagen. D. 42 cm. Purchased 1953.

A898 Jane Craufurd

Ground floor, room 18.
C. 1798-1884. Daughter of the Scottish Baronet James Gregan Craufurd.
Bust. Marble version (Thorvaldsen) of A307 (Rome 1818). Inscribed: "AT". H. 55 cm. Damaged by fire. Presented in 1953 by Brigadier General Sir Standish G. Craufurd.

A899 Mathias Saxtorph

1740-1800. Danish obstetrician.
Bust. Plaster cast of the marble bust in the Rigshospital, Copenhagen, commissioned from Thorvaldsen in 1800 shortly after Saxtorph's death. H. 52 cm. Purchased 1953.

A900 Edmund Bourke

1761-1821. Danish diplomat in Naples.
Bust. Executed in marble in Rome 1800 by Thorvaldsen, probably from a model by the Italian sculptor Domenico Cardelli (1767-1797). H. 45,1 cm. Presented in 1955 by Madame Wanda Krosinski, Brussels, in memory of her Danish grandmother, Madame Alix Dolez Castonier.

A901 Night with Her Children, Sleep and Death

Ground floor, room 8.
Relief. Marble version (Thorvaldsen) of A369 (Rome 1815). Inscribed: "AT". D. 80,5 cm. Presented in 1959 by Henrik Kaufmann, Danish Ambassador to the United States, in memory of his mother, Mathilde, nee von Bernus (1866-1922), the reliefs having been in her childhood home, "Schlösschen", Bockenheim, near Frankfurt-on-Main, for more than a century.

A902 Day: Aurora with the Genius of Light.

Ground floor, room 8.
Relief. Marble version (Thorvaldsen) of A370 (Rome 1815). D. 80 cm. Presented in 1959 by Henrik Kaufmann, Danish Ambassador to the United States, in memory of his mother, Mathilde, nee von Bernus (1866-1922), the reliefs having been in her childhood home, "Schlösschen", Bockenheim, near Frankfurt-on-Main, for more than a century.

A903 Mathias Saxtorph

1740-1800. Danish obstetrician.
Oval portrait medallion. Probably an original plaster model, bronzed. Inscribed: "B. Thorvaldsen Fec 1793". Below the portrait: "Ham Signer Moderen/Med Spœde Barn i Favn/Og Froe Staar Manden Hos/ Og Signer Saxtorphs Navn/ XXIX October MDCCLXXXXIII Rahbek". Copenhagen 1793. H. 49,5 cm. W. 42,7 cm. Purchased 1962.

A904 Elisabeth Christine Saxtorph

1746-1823. Née Sibrand, married to Mathias Saxtorph.
Oval portrait medallion. Probably an original plaster model, bronzed. Inscribed: "B. Thorvaldsen Fe(c) 1793". Below the portrait: "Ey Foed For Sig Alleene/XXIX October MDCCLXXXXIII Rahbek". Copenhagen 1793. H. 49,5 cm. W. 42,7 cm. Purchased 1962.

A905 Night with Her Children, Sleep and Death

Relief. Marble version (Thorvaldsen) of A369 (Rome 1817) executed 1842. D. 79 cm. See also A901. Purchased 1965.

A906 Day: Aurora with the Genius of Light.

Relief. Marble version of A370 (Rome 1815) executed in 1842 in Thorvaldsens studio. D. 83,5 cm. See also A902. Purchased 1965.

A907 Child's Head

Relief. Unfired clay. Fragment of the clay model for A596 (Copenhagen 1838). H. 9 cm. Purchased 1966.

A908 Head of an Angel

Relief. Unfired clay. Fragment of the clay model for A593 (Rome 1842). H. 12,3 cm. Purchased 1973.

A909 Napoleon I

Ground floor, southern corridor.
1769-1821. Emperor of France 1804-14.
Bust. Original plaster model. Rome c. 1830. H. 100 cm. Marble version, see A732 and A867. See also A252 Purchased 1974.

A910 Childhood - Spring

Relief. Marble version (Thorvaldsen) of A642 (Rome 1836). Inscribed: "Thorvaldsen F". D. 68 cm. See also A638. Presented in 1977 by the estate of Dr. Boje Benzon.

A911 Cupid and the Graces

Statue. Plaster cast. The original plaster model A29, Rome 1817-18. H. 172 cm. See also A894. Entered in the inventory in 1977.

A912 Cupid and the Graces

Statue, damaged. Plaster cast. The original plaster model A29, Rome 1817-18. H. 167 cm. See also A894. Entered in the inventory in 1977.

A913 Unknown Lady

Portrait medallion. Original plaster model (?), painted. Inscribed: "B. Thorvaldsen Fec. 179(5)". Copenhagen, probably 1795. D. 43 cm. Purchased 1982.

A 914 Cupid Resting

Oval relief. Plaster cast of the original plaster model A 756. H. 75,6 cm. W. 56 cm. Presented to the Museum in 1988.

A 915 Peter Wilhelm Kolderup Rosenvinge

1816–1820. Danish; son of the jurist, Professor J.L.A. Kolderup Rosenvinge.
Bust. Painted plaster cast of a posthumous bust modelled after a death mask in Copenhagen 1820. Not executed in marble. Original model lost. H. 42 cm. Purchased 1993.

A 916 Venus with the Apple Awarded by Paris

Statue. Reduced marble version of A 12. Possibly from Thorvaldsen's later years. H. 90,6 cm. Purchased 1994.

A 917 Brother and Sister Leaving Their Mother on Erth

Relief. Plaster cast. The original plaster model A161, Rome 1835. H. 172 cm. W. 240 cm. Plaster cast of the marble version executed for the tomb of the children of Princess Helena Poninska in the Palace Chapel in Czerwonogród. Now in the State Museum of Lvov. Purchased 1995.

Dep. 21 The Seasons

Relief. Original plaster model. Copenhagen 1794. Modelled for Prince Frederik's (later Christian X's) Palace at Amalienborg, form a composition by N. A. Abildgaard. H. 57,5 cm. W. 93,5 cm. On loan from the Royal Museum of Fine Arts.

Dep. 22. The Hours

Relief. Original plaster model. Copenhagen 1794. Modelled for Prince Frederik's (later Christian X's) Palace at Amalienborg, from a composition by N. A. Abildgaard. H. 57,5 cm. W 94 cm. On loan from the Royal Museum of Fine Arts.

Dep. 23. Venus and Cupid

Sketch model. Plaster cast of the bozetto in terracotta in the Hirschsprung Collection, Copenhagen. Modelled in 1827(?) in Rome. H. 23,7 cm. W. 40,8 cm. On loan from the Hirschsprung Collection.

Dep. 26. The Seasons

Relief. Plaster cast, painted, of the original plaster model Dep. 21, Copenhagen 1794. H. 58 cm. W. 93 cm.

Dep. 36 Jacob Laurids Thrane

Ground floor, room 1.
1785-1819. Danish architect. Bust. Marble version of A881 (Rome c. 1806) completed in 1807 in Rome. H. 58,5 cm. On loan from Nordjyllands Kunstmuseum, Ålborg.

Catalogue of Paintings

Where not otherwise stated, the painting belonged to Thorvaldsen and came to the Museum according to the terms of his will.

If not otherwise specified, the medium is oil on canvas.

Abildgaard, Nicolai Abraham
Born Copenhagen 1743, died Spurveskjul, Frederiksdal, 1809.

B 427 Cupid playing the Lyre. Painted c. 1782. 28,5 x 23,4 cm. Purchased 1916.

Acquaroni,
See Aquaroni

Agricola, Filippo
Born Urbino 1776, died Rome 1857.

B 98 Portrait of Cardinal Ercole Consalvi, copied from Thomas Lawrence's full-length portrait of the Cardinal at Windsor Castle (1819). 54,9 x 41,9 cm.

Amerling, Friedrich von
Born Vienna 1803, died ibid. 1887.

B 105 Portrait of a Roman peasant. Signed "Fr. Amerling 1838". 54,9 x 44,5 cm.

B435 Portrait of Thorvaldsen. Study for Cat. No. 353 in the Liechtenstein Gallery, Vienna, probably painted 1842. 49 x 39,5 cm.

Andersen, Christian Emil
Born Copenhagen 1817, died ibid. 1845.

B195 The Good Samaritan 1843. Exhibited 1844. 112,5 x 94,2 cm.

Anesi, Paolo
Born Rome c. 1725, died ibid. 1766.

B33 Landscape. 49,7 x 64,1 cm. Attribution, formerly ascribed to Andrea Locatelli.

Anguissola, Sofonisba
Born Cremona 1527, died Palermo 1625.

B9 Portrait of a lady. Painted on slate. Diameter 11,8 cm.

Aquaroni, Antonio
Born Rome c. 1800, died ibid. 1874.

B58 Ponte Cestio in Rome. Painted 1836. 32 x 40,5 cm.

Baldi, Lazzaro
Born Pistoia c. 1623, died Rome 1703.

B27 Boreas and Oreithyia. 51 x 39,8 cm. Attribution.

Balsgaard, Carl Wilhelm
Born Copenhagen 1812, died ibid. 1893.

B311 Portrait of the sculptor Hermann Ernst Freund. Copy of a portrait by C. A. Jensen, painted in Rome 1819, in the Royal Museum of Fine Arts, Copenhagen (Inv. 1212). 11,8 x 8,4 cm.

B312 Portrait of Thorvaldsen. Copy from 1843 of a portrait by C. W. Eckersberg, painted in Rome 1814, in the Academy of Fine Arts, Copenhagen. 14,4 x 11,8 cm.

Baratta, Francesco
Born Genoa 1805, died ibid. c. 1870.

B59 Italian winegrower and his daughter. 137,3 x 98,1 cm.

Barbieri, Giovanni Francesco (Guercino)
Born Cento 1591, died Bologna 1666.

B20 Young girl reading. 35,3 x 26,2 cm.

Barnekow, Robert Gabriel Adolph
Born Faaborg 1848, died New Zealand 1931.

B445 Room 42 in the Thorvaldsen Museum with Thorvaldsen's furniture. Signed "1878. R. B.". 38 x 52 cm. Purchased 1951.

Bartolo, Taddeo di
See Taddeo di Bartolo

Bassano il Giovane, Francesco (da Ponte)
Born Bassano 1549 (?), died Venice 1592.

B10 Genre scene, in the background the Agony in the Garden (?). Signed "BASS.^{S}F.". 94,2 x 131 cm.

Bassano, Jacopo, after
B25 The Descent of the Holy Ghost. Copy of a painting by Jacopo Bassano in the Museo Civico, Bassano. 60,2 x 32,7 cm.

Bassi, Giovanni Battista
Born Massa Lombarda 1784, died Rome 1852.

B60 Woodland scene with pool. Signed "G. B. Bassi f. sul vero 1816". 96,8 x 119 cm.

B61 Road running between garden walls near Terni. Signed "G. B. Bassi f. sul vero 1820". 49,1 x 61,5 cm.

B62 Forest track. Signed "G. B. Bassi studio sul vero 1824". 68 x 61,5 cm.

B63 View of the ruins of the imperial palaces, Rome. Signed "G. B. Bassi f. Romœ". 47,1 x 37,2 cm.

B86 See Pacetti, Michelangelo.

Bendz, Wilhelm Ferdinand
Born Odense 1804, died Vicenza 1832.

B 197 Artists at an evening gathering in Finck's coffee-house, Munich. Signed "W. Bendz München 1832". 94,8 x 136,6 cm.

Bianchi, Giovanni, after
B14 The Virgin and Child. Copy of a painting in the Church of Madonna della Ghiara, Reggio Emilia, by Giovanni Bianchi after a drawing by Lelio Orsi. Painted on copper. 18,3 x 15,1 cm.

Bloemen, Jan Franz van (Orizonte)
Born Antwerp 1662, died Rome 1749.

B49 Landscape. 73,2 x 60,2 cm. Attribution.

B50 Landscape. 37 x 48,4 cm. Attribution .

Blunck, Ditlev Conrad
Born Münsterdorf, Holstein, 1798, died Hamburg 1854.

B34 The Virgin and Child. Copy of a painting by Pietro Perugino in the Detroit Institute of Arts. 84,3 x 71,2 cm.

B35 Madonna del Granduca, 1831. Copy of a painting by Raphael in the Palazzo Pitti, Florence. 85 x 57,5 cm.

B54 Portrait of a man. Copy of a portrait by Bartholomeus van der Helst. 69,3 x 52,3 cm.

B198 Noah and his family in the Ark. Signed "D. C. Blunck Roma 1835". 69,3 x 90,2 cm.

B199 Danish artists at the Osteria La Gensola, Rome (To the right, Thorvaldsen). Signed "D. C. Blunck Roma 1837". 74,5 x 99,4 cm.

B404 Two German doctors, Karl von Pfeuffer and Lorenz Melchior Geist. Signed "DCB" and inscribed "Zur dankbaren Erinnerung der mit Euch in Rom zusammen verlebten Monathe August und September 1837". Painted on paper. 15 x 18,7 cm.

Boesen, August Wilhelm
Born Vigerslev 1812, died Bologna 1857.

B200 Danish landscape. Signed "A. W. B." 32 x 44,5 cm.

Brill, Paul
Born Antwerp 1554, died Rome 1626.

B400 Mountain landscape. 77,5 x 109 cm. Attribution.

Bruegel (the Elder), Jan
Born Brussels 1568, died Antwerp 1625.

B44 Aeneas and the Cumaean Sibyl in the Underworld. (The painting was formerly called Hell). Painted on copper. 26,8 x 35,3 cm. Attribution.

B45 The Temptation of St. Anthony. Painted on copper. 19,6 x 24, 8 cm. Attribution.

Buntzen, Heinrich Christian August
Born Kiel 1803, died Ordrup 1892.

B201 Oak trees by a pool. Signed "Heinr. Buntzen inv. et pinx. München 1840". 115,7 x 161,5 cm.

B202 Casa del Portinaio, formerly called the Villa of Raphael, in the gardens of the Villa Borghese, Rome. Signed "H. Buntzen pinx. Hafniœ 1843". Painted on paper. 25,5 x 32 cm.

B203 The manor house of Nysø, to the left Thorvaldsen in front of his studio. Signed "HB 1843". 55,5 x 71,2 cm.

B204 Danish landscape. Signed "Heinrich Buntzen 1844". 119 x 160,8 cm.

Bürkel, Heinrich
Born Pirmasens 1802, died Munich 1869.

B106 Scene in front of an Italian osteria. Signed "H. Bürkel. 1831". 51 x 74,5 cm.

B107 The performing bears come to an Italian village. Signed "H. Bürkel Rom 1831". 57,5 x 74,5 cm.

Bœrentzen, Emilius Ditlev
Born Copenhagen 1799, died ibid. 1868.

B205 Portrait of the actress Johanne Luise Heiberg. Painted 1841. 122,5 x 94,5 cm.

Cades, Giuseppe
Born Rome 1750, died ibid. 1799.

B39 La Disputa del SS Sacramento. Copy of Raphael's fresco in the Stanza della Segnatura in the Vatican, Rome. 100,6 x 137,5 cm.

Caffi, Ippolito
Born Belluno 1809, died in the battle of Lissa 1866.

B64 *Moccoli* Evening in the Via del Corso during the carnival in Rome. Painted 1834. 38 x 47 cm.

B65 *La Girandola* fireworks from Castel Sant'Angelo during the Easter celebrations in Rome. Signed "Caffi". 36,6 x 46,5 cm.

B66 A Venetian gala night. 22 x 29 cm.

Camuccini, Vincenzo
Born Rome 1771, died ibid. 1844.

B67 Christ blessing the children. Painted on wood, c. 1826. 22,9 x 34 cm.

Carracci, Annibale, after
B23 The penitent Mary Magdalene. Reduced copy of a painting by Annibale Carracci in the Galleria Doria Pamphili, Rome, Inv. No. 203. 32 x 41,9 cm.

Carstens, Asmus Jacob
Born S.]ürgen near Schleswig 1754, died Rome 1798.

See Catel, B299.

Carus, Carl Gustav
Born Leipzig 1789, died Dresden 1869.

B108 A prehistoric barrow by moonlight, Nobben on the island of Rügen. Painted on paper. 7,8 x 11,2 cm.

Castelli, Alessandro
Born Rome 1809, died ibid. 1902.
B68 Landscape. 29,4 x 44,5 cm.

Castello, Francesco da
Born in the Netherlands c. 1540, died Rome 1621.
B13 The Ecstasy of St. Francis. 131,1 x 96,8 cm. Attribution.

Catel, Franz
Born Berlin 1778, died Rome 1856.
B109 A Neapolitan fisherman and his family. 48,4 x 62,2 cm.

B110 A grotto in Mœcenas' Villa, Tivoli. 54,3 x 70 cm.

B111 Night piece, from the closing scene of "René". by Chateaubriand. 62,8 x 73,8 cm.

B112 Landscape at sunset. 15,7 x 24,1 cm.

B299 The Golden Age. Copy of a drawing by A. J. Carstens, painted 1812 by Catel (landscape) and John James Rubby (figures). 54,9 x 87,6 cm.

Chauvin, Pierre Athanase
Born Paris 1774, died Rome 1832.

B87 View of the gardens of the Villa Falconieri, Frascati. Signed "Chauvin à Frascati. 1810". 62,2 x 74,5 cm.

B88 View of the gardens of the Villa d'Este, Tivoli. Signed "Chauvin à Tivoli 1811". 62,8 x 73,8 cm.

B89 Grottaferrata in the Alban Hills. Signed "Chauvin 1811 à Grotta Ferrata". 62,2 x 74,5 cm.

Cornelius, Peter
Born Düsseldorf 1783, died Berlin 1867.
B113 The Entombment of Christ. Painted on wood. 34 x 47,1 cm.

Correggio, Antonio Allegri,
after
B42 The marriage of St. Catherine. Copy of a painting by Correggio in the Louvre, Paris, Cat.No. 1117. 98,1 x 100,7 cm.

Dahl, Carl Michael
Born Faaborg 1812, died Copenhagen 1865.

B206 The frigate Thetis and the corvette Flora on the river Tagus. Painted 1844. 120,4 x 181 cm.

B207 Larsens Plads, the harbour of Copenhagen. Exhibited 1840. 54,9 x 70,6 cm.

B451 A. F. Tscherning showing two peasants the statue of Vulcan in the Thorvaldsen Museum. Purchased 1977. 38 x 38 cm.

Dahl, Johan Christian
Born Bergen 1788, died Dresden 1857.

B128 See Koch, Joseph Anton.

B177 The Bay of Naples by moonlight. Signed "J. Dahl 1821". 49,7 X 68 cm.

B178 The Bay of Naples by moonlight. Signed "J. Dahl 1821". 34 x 48,4 cm.

B179 Vesuvius in eruption. Moonlight. Signed "Dahl 1821". 24,8 x 39,8 cm.

B180 Grotto by the Bay of Naples. Moonlight. Signed "Dahl Juni 1821". 22,2 x 33,4 cm.

B181 St. Peter's Square by moonlight. Signed "Dahl 1821". 37,9 x 30,1 cm.

B182 Country road near La Storta, Italy. Signed "d. 7. april 1821". 22,9 x 32,7 cm.

B183 A waterfall, Italy. Signed "Rom d. 26. Juni 1821". 36,6 x 47,1 cm.

B184 Norwegian mountain landscape with waterfall. Signed "Dahl 1821". 98,8 x 137,3 cm.

B185 Norwegian landscape, Jordalsnuten. Signed "Dahl 1821". 35,3 X 47,1 cm.

B186 Norwegian mountain valley. Signed "Dahl Mai 1821" (or 1827). 96,8 x 134,6 cm.

B187 The seaward approach to Copenhagen. Signed "Dahl 1830". 40,5 x 55,5 cm.

B188 The coast at Laurvig, Norway. Signed "Dahl 1840". Painted on paper. 7,8 x 13,1 cm.

B189 Landscape from Telemark, Norway. Signed "Dahl 1840". Painted on paper. 7,8 x 13,1 cm.

Dandini, Pier
Born Florence 1646, died ibid. 1712.

B17 The penitent Mary Magdalene. 51,7 x 44,5 cm. Attribution.

Diofebi, Francesco
Born Narni 1781, died Rome 1851.

B69 Penitents in a Roman church. Signed "F. Diofebj f.". 46,5 x 37,9 cm.

B70 The side steps from the Capitol to the church of S. Maria in Aracoeli, Rome. Signed "Diofebi f. 1825". 99,4 x 73,8 cm.

B71 The ruined Temple of Mars Ultor, Rome. Signed "Diofebj f. 1826". 61,5 x 47,7 cm.

B72 St.Joseph's Day (March 19) in Rome. Signed "Diofebi f. 1832". 61,5 x 74,5 cm.

B73 The opening of Raphael's grave in 1833, to the right Thorvaldsen as representative of the Accademia di San Luca, Rome. Signed "F. Diofebi f. 1836". 54,9 x 70 cm.

B74 The approach to the Villa Borghese, Rome. Signed "Diofebi f. 1838". 37,9 x 47,1 cm.

B75 Children playing in a Roman street. Signed "Diofebi f. 1838". 37,2 x 47,1 cm.

B76 Italian monastery in the mountains. Signed "Diofebi f. 1839". 37,2 x 47,1 cm.

B77 Night piece, nuns in a convent. Signed "Diofebj". 36,6 x 47,1 cm.

Dreyer, Dankvart Christian Magnus
Born Assens 1816, died Barløse 1852.

B208 View of the coast near Aarhus. Signed "Dreyer". Painted c. 1839. 93,5 x 129,4 cm.

Dutch School
17th century.

B47 Man with a wine-glass. Painted on copper. 13,7 x 11,1 cm.

Eckersberg, Christoffer Wilhelm
Born Blaakrog, Varnœs, 1783, died Copenhagen 1853.

B209 Sleeping woman in antique dress. Fragment of a painting "The Dream of Alcyone" (Ovid's Metamorphoses, XI, 410-748). Signed "Roma 1813". 44,5 x 39,2 cm.

B210 Female harvester in antique dress. Fragment of a painting "Vertumnus and Pomona" Painted in Rome 1813-16. 36 x 19,6 cm.

B211 A Roman beggar. Painted in Rome 1815. 29,4 x 20,9 cm.

B212 Socrates expounding a proposition to Alcibiades. Painted in Rome 1813-16. 32,7 x 24,1 cm.

B213 Hector's farewell to Andromache. Painted in Rome 1813-16. 49,1 x 34,6 cm.

B214 St. Peter's Square. Painted in Rome 1813-16. 31,4 x 26,8 cm.

B215 The Virgin and Child, enthroned on the clouds. Free copy of the upper part of Raphaels "Madonna di Foligno" in the Vatican. Painted in Rome 1816. 35,3 x 28,2 cm.

B216 Portrait of Frederik VI. Replica of a portrait made in 1820. Painted 1839. Signed "Ætatis L. MDCCCXX. E. fecit". 59,5 x 51 cm.

B217 Thorvaldsen's arrival in the Copenhagen roadstead, September 17th 1838. Painted 1839. Signed "E". 71,9 x 96,2 cm.

B405 The Colosseum. Painted in Rome 1813-16. 32 x 25,5 cm.

B406 Portrait of a Lady, probably the Roman model Maddalena. Copy, probably by a pupil, of a painting from 1814 in the Hirschsprung Collection, Copenhagen. 26,5 x 19,3 cm. Presented to the Museum 1868.

B419 Portrait of Thorvaldsen. Replica of B454. 50,3 x 40,3 cm. Bequested to the Museum 1855, entered the collections in 1871.

B454 Portrait of Thorvaldsen. Painted 1820 in Copenhagen. Inscribed on the Stretcher: "Albert Thorwaldsen malet af Eckersberg Mai 1820". 49,7 x 40 cm. Presented to the Museum 1994.

Eggers, Carl.
Born Neustrelitz 1787, died ibid. 1863.

B36 La Madonna del garofano. Copy of a painting, formerly ascribed to Raphael. Painted on wood. 28,8 x 23,5 cm.

B37 The violin player. Copy of a painting by Sebastiano del Piombo in the E. de Rothschild Collection, Paris. 70,6 x 54,9 cm.

Eggink, Johann Leberecht
Born Kurland 1787, died Mitau 1867.

B38 The vision of Ezekiel. Copy of a painting by Raphael in the Palazzo Pitti, Florence, Cat.No. 174. Painted on wood. 40,5 x 29,4 cm.

Elsasser, Friedrich August
Born Berlin 1810, died Rome 1845.

B114 View from the ancient theatre in Taormina. Painted 1838. Signed "A. Elsasser Roma". 68 x 102,6 cm.

Fearnley, Thomas
Born Frederikshald 1802, died Munich 1842.

B190 Norwegian landscape, Marumfoss. Signed "Th. Fearnley 1833". 124,9 x 174,6 cm.

B191 The sea at Palermo. Signed "TF Palermo. 24. Juny 1833". 18,3 x 25,5 cm.

B192 Capri viewed from Sorrento. Signed "TF Sorrent. 28. Aug. 33" (1833). 15,1 x 22,2 cm.

B193 View of Elsinore, summer. Signed "Th. Fearnley 1833". 74,5 x 100 cm.

B194 View of Elsinore, winter. Signed "Th. Fearnley 1833". 74,5 x 100 cm.

Ferrarese School
Late 16th century.

B7 The Virgin with her family. 56,2 x 75,4 cm. Stylistically close to Sigismondo Scarsella.

Fiorentino
See Pseudo-Pier Francesco Fiorentino.

Fiorenzo di Lorenzo
Born c. 1440, died 1522/5. Active in Umbria.

B4 Two panels from an altar-piece, showing St. Eligius and John the Baptist. On the back a circle inscribed in a rhombus and in the corners an axe, a hammer and two knives. Tempera on wood. 62,8 x 45,8 cm. Attribution.

Fioroni, Luigi
Born S. Fiora 1795, died Rome 1864.

B78 Evening scene at a Roman osteria by the Piazza della Trinità dei Monti. Signed "Luigi Fironi fece 1830". 74,5 x 100 cm.

B79 Pope Pius VIII carried in procession through the colonnade of St. Peter's. Rome. Painted 1829-30. 50,3 x 62,2 cm.

Flemish School
17th century.

B51 A ferry. 41,9 X 60,2 cm. Formerly ascribed to "the manner of A. F. Boudewyns and Peeter Bout".

B52 Road beside a river. 41,9 x 60,2 cm. Formerly ascribed to "the manner of A. F. Boudewyns and Peeter Bout".

B53 Crowd scene. 40,5 x 52,3 cm. Formerly ascribed to "the manner of A. F. Boudewyns and Peeter Bout".

Flor, Ferdinand
Born Hamburg 1793, died Rome 1881.

B115 Portrait of Elisa Paulsen, Thorvaldsen's daughter. Painted 1838. 74,5 X 62,8 cm.

Foltz, Philipp von
Born Bingen 1805, died Munich 1877.

B116 Sleeping Italian beggar girl in a Roman church. Signed "Foltz inv. 1836 Rom". 74,5 x 62,2 cm.

B117 Composition sketch illustrating Johann Ludwig Uhland's poem "Des Sängers Fluch". Signed "Foltz inv. Roma 1837". 79,8 x 60,8 cm.

Francesco, Beniamino de
Born Naples, died Dinard, St. Malo. 1869.

B80 Italian landscape. Signed "De Francesco 1836". 41,2 x 60,2 cm.

B81 Italian landscape with Æneas and the Cumaean Sibyl. Signed "De Francesco 1838". Painted on wood. 71,9 x 90,2 cm.

Friedlœnder, Julius
Born Copenhagen 1810, died ibid. 1861.

B218 Scene in a fishing hamlet (Taarbœk) in Zealand. Signed "J. F. 1839". 53,6 x 64,1 cm.

Galster, Henrik Ludvig
Born Nørre Sundby 1826, died Copenhagen 1901.

B439 Portrait of Thorvaldsen. Reduced copy of Horace Vernet's portrait (B95). Signed "H. L. Galster". Painted on ivory. 8,3 x 8,6 cm. Presented to the Museum 1935.

Gazzarini, Tommaso
Born Leghorn 1790, died Florence 1853.

B82 The infant Christ. Painted 1822. 17,7 x 24,8 cm.

Gegenbauer, Joseph Anton
Born Wangen 1800, died Rome 1876.

B314 Hercules and Omphale. Painted 1826. Fresco, transferred to canvas. 202,7 x 155,6 cm.

German School (?)
18th century.

B57 A shoemaker's shop. 62,2 x 73,8 cm. When in Thorvaldsen's possession ascribed to William Hogarth.

German School (?)
18th century.

B414 Portrait of a man. Oval miniature. 2,4 x 2 cm.

Gertner, Johan Vilhelm
Born Copenhagen 1818, died ibid. 1871.

B430 Thorvaldsen in his studio. Painted on wood, c. 1839. 33 x 24,5 cm. Presented to the Museum 1923.

Dep. 35 Thorvaldsen modelling the bust of Adam Oehlenschläger. Painted 1842. 121,4 x 93,5 cm. Lent by Nordjyllands Kunstmuseum, Ålborg.

Gimignani, Giacinto
Born Pistoia 1611, died Rome 1681.

B21 The Virgin and Child. 67,4 x 51 cm. Attribution.

Giovannini, Vincenzo
Born Todi 1816, died Rome 1868.
B96 A chemist in his laboratory.
73,2 x 98,1 cm.

Glowacki, Jan Nepomucen
Born Cracow 1802, died ibid. 1847.
B174 Tyrolean (or Bavarian) landscape. Signed "I. Nep. Glowacki Roma 1835". Painted on paper. 34,6 x 45,1 cm.

Gorawski, Apollinari,
see: Horawski, Apollinarij.

Grove, Fritz Nordahl
Born Copenhagen 1822, died ibid. 1885.
B219 View from Baunebjerg by Horsens Fjord. Exhibited 1843. 50,1 x 76,5 cm.

Gudin, Théodore
Born Paris 1802, died Boulogne sur-Seine 1880.
B90 The coast near Naples. Signed "T. Gudin Rome 1837". 40,5 x 61,5 cm.

Guérard, Bernhard von
Born Düsseldorf, died Naples 1836.
B447 Portrait of Thorvaldsen. Replica of a painting from 1831 in the Museo di Capodimonte, Naples. Signed "B. Ch. Guerard 1834". Painted on wood. 19,4 x 15,2 cm.

Guercino,
see Barbieri, Giovanni Francesco.

Hansen, Carl Christian Constantin
Born Rome 1804, died Copenhagen 1880.
B220 View of the Temple of Poseidon at Paestum. Painted 1839. 30,1 x 34 cm.
B415 Portrait of the architect M. G. Bindesbøll. Signed "Const. H. 1849". 118 x 95 cm. Commissioned by the board of directors of the Thorvaldsen Museum.
B416 Portrait of Jonas Collin, titular Privy Councillor, Chairman of the Thorvaldsen Museum Committee. Signed "Const. H. 1851". 105,8 x 84,5 cm. Presented to the Museum 1851.
B442 View of the Thorvaldsen Museum. Signed "CH. 58" (1858). 36,3 x 43,8 cm. Presented to the Museum 1938.

Harder, Johannes (Hans)
Born Copenhagen 1792, died Sorø 1873.
B221 Landscape with the Mill at Bromme near Sorø. Painted on wood. 30,1 x 43,2 cm.

Heideck, Karl Wilhelm von
Born Saaralben 1788, died Munich 1861.
B118 Scene from the defence of a Spanish town during a guerrilla war. Signed "C. v. Hdk p^r $\frac{4}{1841}$". 71,2 x 92,8 cm.

Hellesen, Lars Julius August
Born Copenhagen 1823, died ibid. 1877.

B222 Danish landscape. Signed "Julius Hellesen 1843". 94,8 x 126,1 cm.

B223 The coast at the fishing hamlet of Flade near Frederikshavn. Signed "jH. 1842". 22,2 x 35,3 cm.

Henning, Adolph
Born Berlin 1809, died ibid. 1900.

B119 Portrait of the model Fortunata Segatori from Subiaco as poetess. Painted between 1833 and 1835. 46,5 x 46,5 cm.

Henriques, Salomon (Sally) Ruben
Born Copenhagen 1815, died ibid. 1886.

B407 Portrait of a sailor. Painted 1840. 50,7 x 46,8 cm.

Hensel, Wilhelm
Born Trebbin 1794, died Berlin 1861.

B437 Portrait of Thorvaldsen. Signed on the back "W. Hensel ad viv. pinxt.". 54,3 x 43,8 cm. Presented to the Museum 1934.

Hering, George Edwards
Born London 1805, died ibid. 1879.

B120 A street in Smyrna. Signed "G. H. 33" (1833). 42,5 x 37,2 cm.

Heuss, Franz Eduard
Born Oggersheim 1808, died Bodenheim 1880.

Dep. 2. Portrait of Thorvaldsen. Signed: "Heuss 1834", on the back: "Hanc Alberti Thorvaldsen effigiem Romœ pinxit anno 1834 Ed. Heuss". 74,5 x 62,2 cm. Lent by the Ny Carlsberg Glyptotek.

Holbech, Niels Peter
Born at sea 1804, died Karlshamn 1889.

B224 A young Italian woman with her children and an old woman spinning, Nettuno. Signed "NPH 1831". 62,2 x 50,3 cm.

B225 A pilgrim sitting by a fountain in the Via dell' Arco Scuro, Rome. Probably painted between 1830 and 1834. 64,1 x 49,7 cm.

Hopfgarten, August
Born Berlin 1807, died ibid. 1896.

B122 The miracle of St. Elizabeth. Signed "A. Hopfgartn Rom 1832". 62,2 x 44,5 cm.

Horawski, Apollinarij Hilarjevitsch
Born Minsk 1833, died St. Petersburg 1900.

B441 Portrait of Thorvaldsen. Copy painted 1852 after a portrait by Orest Kiprenski from 1833 in the Hermitage, Leningrad. 65 x 54,5 cm. Presented to the Museum 1937.

Hornemann, Christian
Born Copenhagen 1765, died ibid. 1844.

B310 Portrait of Thorvaldsen. Signed "Hornemann". Painted on ivory. 10,9 x 8,2 cm.

Høyer, Christian Fœdder
Born Rerslev near Roskilde 1775, died Copenhagen 1855.

B226 Cupid received by Anacreon. From Anacreontea, Song 3. Probably painted between 1808 and 1811. 74,5 x 98,8 cm.

B408 Ossian carrying his dead brother Fillan, followed by Fingal's dog Bran. From Songs of Ossian, Temora 6. 51 x 66,5 cm.

B409 The metamorphosis of Lucius. From Apuleius' The Golden Ass. 51 x 68 cm.

Ingemann, Lucie Marie
Born Copenhagen 1792, died Sora 1868.

B410 A gardener. 35,5 x 31,5 cm.

B429 The Apotheosis of Thorvaldsen. 77,5 x 67 cm. Presented to the Museum 1922.

Italian School
16th century.

B8 Portrait of a man. Painted on wood. 44,5 x 32,7 cm.

Italian School
17th century.

B19 The Virgin and Child with St. Martha. 45,8 x 37,9 cm.

Italian School
17th century.

B22 St. Joseph with the flowering rod. 62,8 x 48,4 cm.

Italian School
17th century.

B24 The Holy Family. 95,5 x 72,6 cm.

Italian School
17th century.

B26 The dream of St.Joseph. 69,3 x 90,2 cm.

Italian School
17th century.

B30 Buildings along a coastline. Supraporte painting. 23,5 x 109,3 cm.

Italian School
17th century.

B306 The ecstasy of St. Francis. Painted on leather. 19,6 x 15,7 cm.

Italian School
16th century?

B313 Head of a saint. Painted on chalk. 28,8 x 21,5 cm.

Jensen, Carl Vilhelm Marius
Born Ringsted 1819, died Liljedal, Orslev, 1882.

B228 The Manor of Gisselfeld, Zealand. Signed "C. V. Jensen 1839". 50,3 x 74,5 cm.

Jensen, Christian Albrecht
Born Bredsted near Husum (Holstein) 1792, died Copenhagen 1870.

B227 Portrait of the flower painter Claudius Ditlev Fritzsch. Painted c. 1835. 24,1 x 18,9 cm.

B432 Portrait of Baroness Christine Stampe, nee Dalgas. Signed "C. A. Jensen 1827". 64,2 x 50,8 cm. Presented to the Museum 1924.

B433 Portrait of Thorvaldsen. Signed "C. A. Jensen pinxit 1839". 28,8 x 22,8 cm. Presented to the Museum 1926.

B444 Portrait of the poet Ludvig Bødtcher. Signed "C. A. Jensen 1836". 36 x 28,8 cm. Presented to the Museum 1942.

Jensen, Johan Laurentz
Born Gentofte 1800, died Copenhagen 1856.

B230 Flowers in a vase on a marble tabletop. Signed "I. L. Jensen 1833". 22,2 x 28,8 cm.

B231 Fruit on a marble tabletop. Signed "I. L. Jensen 1833". 24,1 x 32,7 cm.

B232 Flowers in an antique vase. Signed "I. L. Jensen Roma 1834". 61,5 x 50,3 cm.

B233 Still life on a kitchen tabletop. Signed "I. L. Jensen Roma 1835". 90,9 x 75,2 cm.

B234 Flowers in an antique vase. Signed "I. L. Jensen 1838". 90,2 X 71,9 cm.

B236 White lilies and roses. Signed "1843". Painted on wood. 58,8 x 42,5 cm.

Jensen, Johannes
Born Copenhagen 1818, died ibid. 1873.

B229 Portrait of an old sailor. Signed "Joh:Jensen 1843". 39,8 x 32,7 cm.

B434 Portrait of Thorvaldsen. 14,9 x 12,7 cm. Presented to the Museum 1928.

B436 Portrait of Thorvaldsen. 12,9 x 12 cm. Purchased 1933.

Juel, Jens
Born Funen 1745, died Copenhagen 1802.

B237 View of the Little Belt from Hindsgavl, Funen. Probably painted c. 1800. 42 x 62,5 cm.

B238 View of the Little Belt from a hill near Middelfart, Funen. Probably painted c. 1800. 42,3 x 62,5 cm.

B239 View from Veyrier over Lake Geneva towards the Jura mountains. Painted between 1777 and 1779. 116,4 x 86,9 cm.

B315 Portrait of Wilhelmine Bertouch, Lady-in-Waiting. Pastel. 52,3 x 39,2 cm.

Juel, Jens, after
B411 Portrait of the artist's mother, Vilhelmine Elisabeth Juel. Copy of a painting by Juel, probably exhibited 1794, in the Ny Carlsberg Glyptotek, Copenhagen, Inv. No. 900. 47 x 39 cm.

Kaufmann, Hermann
Born Hamburg 1808, died ibid. 1889.

B123 Tyrolean roadside inn. Signed "H. Kaufmann 1843". 36 x 49,1 cm.

Kiprenski, Orest
Born Koporje 1773, died Rome 1836.

B175 Portrait of an Armenian priest. On the back a study of the male nude. 74,5 x 58,8 cm.

Kiœrskou, Frederik Christian
Born Copenhagen 1805, died ibid. 1891.

B240 The Road from Reichenhall to Ramsau in Bavaria. Signed "F. C. Kierskou 1846". 76,5 x 62,8 cm.

Klenze, Leo von
Born Schladen am Harz 1784, died Munich 1864.

B124 The harbour at Pirano, Istria. Signed "L.v.K". Painted 1831. 62,8 x 78,5 cm.

Kloss, Friedrich Theodor
Born Brunswick 1802, died Copenhagen 1876.

B241 Approach to Copenhagen by sea. Signed "T Kloss 1838". 34 x 50,3 cm.

Koch, Joseph Anton
Born Obergiebeln 1768, died Rome 1839.

B125 Apollo among the Thessalian shepherds. Signed "J. K.". Painted 1834-35. 79,1 x 115,7 cm.

B126 Italian landscape with bridge over river, Terni. Signed "J. Koch f.". Painted on wood, around 1830. 35,3 x 49,7 cm.

B127 Landscape from Olevano, to the right a self-portrait. Signed "J. Koch". Painted on wood, ca. 1823. 35,3 x 47,7 cm.

B128 Lauterbrunnertal near Unterseen with a view of the Jungfrau. Probably painted 1821 in collaboration with J. C. Dahl, who inserted the shepherd with his goats. 74,5 x 98,1 cm.

B129 Noah's sacrifice after the Flood. Signed "G. Koch Tyrolese 1815". Painted on wood. 18,9 x 23,5 cm.

B158 See Schick, Gottlieb.

Koop, Andreas Ludvig
Born Copenhagen 1792, died Rome 1849.

B168 Portrait of Thorvaldsen. Copy painted 1828 after a portrait from 1823 by Karl Begas. 103,3 x 73,2 cm.

Krafft, Johan August
Born Altona 1798, died Rome 1829.

B242 Carnival gaiety in a Roman street. Signed "Augt. Krafft 1828". 32,7 x 42,5 cm.

Küchler, Albert
Born Copenhagen 1803, died Rome 1886. Became a monk in 1851 as Fra Pietro.

B243 The death of Correggio, scene from Act V of Adam Oehlenschläger's tragedy "Correggio". Signed "A. Küchler 1834". 83,7 x 74,5 cm.

B244 Domestic scene by Lake Nemi. Signed "A. Küchler. Rom 1837". 95,5 x 81,1 cm.

B245 Colonel and Mrs Paulsen, Thorvaldsen's son-in-law and daughter, with their two children. Signed "A. Küchler Roma 1838". 71,9 x 64,8 cm.

B246 Roman peasants buying a hat for their little son, who is to be an *abbate*. Signed "A. Küchler 1840". 75,9 x 92,8 cm.

B247 A young *abbate* recites his lesson to his sister. Signed "A. Küchler". Painted c. 1838. 44,5 x 37,9 cm.

La Bouère, Tancrède de
Born La Bouère, Jallais, 1801, died Grenoble 1881.

B91 The coast by the Pontine marshes. In the foreground buffaloes. Signed "Labouère à Rome 1838". 100,7 x 168 cm.

Landesio, Eugenio
Born 1809, died 1879. Active in Rome.

B83 Italian landscape. Signed "E. Landesio F. Roma 1838". 74,4 x 92,1 cm.

Larsen, Peter Julius
Born Copenhagen 1818, died Rome 1852.

B248 Portrait of an old sailor. Signed "P. L. 1840". 37,2 x 30,8 cm.

B452 Interior from the Academy of Fine Arts, Copenhagen, with works

by Thorvaldsen. Signed "PJ Larsen 1837". 71,5 x 53 cm. Purchased 1977.

Lazzarini, Giovanni
Born 1769, died 1834. Active in Rome and Lucca.

B84 The Roman aqueduct Aqua Vergine in the courtyard of No. 12 Via del Nazareno. Painted by two artists. Signed "J. (G)... et Lazzarini Amici f-nt Romœ 1823". 60,8 x 73,8 cm.

B97 The choir of the Capuchin Monastery near the Piazza Barberini, Rome. Copy of a painting by Francois Marius Granet. 47,7 x 36,6 cm.

Libert, Georg Emil
Born Copenhagen 1820, died ibid. 1908.

B249 View of the Sound from Langelinie near Copenhagen. Signed "G. E. Libert 1839". 94,2 x 126,1 cm.

B250 Moors near Aalborg. Signed "G. E. Libert 1839". 65,4 x 102,6 cm.

Lindau, Dietrich Wilhelm
Born Dresden 1799, died Rome 1862.

B130 Peasants at Monte Mario on their way to Rome. Signed "Dietrich Lindau Roma 1826". 52,3 x 76,2 cm.

B131 A *Saltarello* being danced in a Roman osteria. Signed "Dietrich Lindau 1827". 50,3 X 71,9 cm.

B424 Portrait of Thorvaldsen. Signed "Lindau f. Romœ". Painted on paper, c. 1827. 17,2 x 14,5 cm.

Löhr, Franz Conrad
Born 1735, died 1812. Active in Hamburg.

B438 Portrait of a man. According to tradition a portrait of Gotskalk Thorvaldsen, Thorvaldsen's father. Signed "F. C. Löhr pinxit 1788". 67 x 53 cm. Purchased 1934.

Lorenzo, Fiorenzo di
see Fiorenzo di Lorenzo.

Lorenzo Monaco,
see Monaco, Lorenzo.

Lund, Johan Ludvig Gebhard
Born Kiel 1777, died Copenhagen 1867.

B251 St. Anne teaching the virgin to read (Friederike Brun and Mimmi Zoega). Painted on wood, 1818. 41,2 x 32,7 cm.

B252 Italian landscape. Painted on wood. 28,8 x 22,9 cm.

B301 Portrait of a lady. 45,8 x 40,3 cm. Attribution.

B412 Sophienholm, the manor house of Constantin Brun. Painted on an iron plate. 26,4 x 21,3 cm.

B448 Portrait of Orsola Polverini Narlinghi, Thorvaldsen's landlady in Rome 1800-04. 14,5 x 11,5 cm. Presented to the Museum 1966.

Lund, Troels
Born Copenhagen 1802, died ibid. 1867.

B300 Portrait of Jørgen Bentzen (1742-1822), porter and model at the Academy of Fine Arts, Copenhagen. 55 x 50 cm.

Lundbye, Johan Thomas
Born Kalundborg 1818, died Bedsted 1848.

B253 Landscape at Arresø, looking towards the sand-dunes at Tisvilde. Signed "JTL 1838". 94,2 x 125,5 cm. Won by Thorvaldsen at the Art Society, Copenhagen, in 1839.

B254 View from Vinderød towards Høbjerg near Frederiksvœrk, with the home af Lundbye's parents. Painted 1839 as companion piece to B253. 94,2 x 125,5 cm.

B255 Dolmen at Raklev, Røsnœs. Signed "JTL Mai 1839". 66,7 X 88,9 cm.

Lunde, Anders Christian
Born Copenhagen 1809, died ibid. 1886.

B256 View of Frederiksberg Palace from the vicinity of Ladegaardsvej, Copenhagen Exhibited 1840. 42,5 x 63,4 cm.

Lœssøe, Thorald
Born Frederikshavn 1816, died Copenhagen 1878.

B257 Valløby Church, Zealand. Signed "Thorald Lœssøe 1839". 73,8 x 109,3 cm.

Magnus, Eduard
Born Berlin 1799, died ibid. 1872.
B132 Portrait of Thorvaldsen in his working clothes. Painted c. 1828. 62,8 x 49,7 cm.

Markó, Carl (Károly)
Born Lócse, Hungary, 1791, died Antella near Florence 1860.

B169 View of Lake Nemi and Monte Cavo. Signed "C. Marko 1834". 74,5 x 99,4 cm.

B170 Landscape with nymphs. Signed "S. Markó 1834". 26,8 x 29,4 cm.

B171 Landscape with nymphs bathing. Signed "C. Markó 1834". 26,8 x 29,4 cm.

B172 Italian mountain scene, women by a fountain. Signed "C. Markó Romœ 1836". 34 x 45,8 cm.

B173 Italian mountain scene, wanderers on a road. Signed "C. Markó Romœ". 1836(?). 34 x 45,8 cm.

Marstrand, Wilhelm Nicolai
Born Copenhagen 1810, died ibid. 1873.
B258 October Festival evening outside the walls of Rome. Signed "W. Marstrand Roma 1839". 90,9 x 123 cm.

B420 *Abbate* jesting with two young girls. Marstrand's last work, painted March 15, 1873. 42 x 55,3 cm. Presented to the Museum 1873.

B421 Portrait of Just Mathias Thiele, Thorvaldsen's biographer. 87,3 x 70,5 cm. Purchased 1874.

Dep. 25 Portrait of the architect M. G. Bindesbøll. Signed "W. M. 1844". 20 x 15 cm. Lent by the Royal Museum of Fine Arts.

Martens, Hans Ditlev Christian
Born Kiel 1795, died ibid. 1864.

B259 The Antique Room at the Academy of Fine Arts, Copenhagen. Signed "H. D. C. Martens pinxit 1824". 92,8 x 74,5 cm.

B260 St. Peter's from the Via Sacra, north of Rome. Painted on paper. 76,5 x 54,3 cm.

B261 The Capitol in Rome, from the colonnade of the Palazzo dei Conservatori. 76,5 x 54,3 cm.

B262 The house of Michelangelo in Rome. Signed "H. D. C. Martens Roma 1833". 57,5 x 71,9 cm.

Dep. 18 Pope Leo XII visits Thorvaldsen's studios near the Piazza Barberini, Rome, on St. Luke's Day (October 18th), 1826. Signed "H. D. C. Martens. Roma". Painted 1830. 100 x 138 cm. Lent by the Royal Museum of Fine Arts.

Melbye, Daniel Herman Anton
Born Copenhagen 1818, died Paris 1875.
B263 A calm morning at sea. Signed "A. Melbye 1840". 47,1 x 57,5 cm.

B264 Dutch koff and ship of the line in a moderate breeze. Signed "Anton Melbye – 1840". 70,6 x 95,5 cm.

B265 Fishing-boats in the Channel.
Signed "Anton Melbye 1844". 19,6
x 27,5 cm.

Meyer, Ernst
Born Altona 1791, died Rome
1861.

B266 A Roman street letter-writer
reading a letter aloud to a young
girl. Signed "18 EM 29". 62,2 x
69,3 cm.

B267 A Roman street letter-writer
writing a letter for a young girl.
Signed "E. M.", on the letter the
date 1827. 62,2 x 69,3 cm.

B268 A Capri fisherman. Signed
"E. Meier Rom". Painted 1844 (?)
and purchased after the death of
Thorvaldsen. 45,8 x 59,5 cm.

B269 A Neapolitan fisherman at his
door. Signed "E Meyer". 49,7 x
39,8 cm.

B270 A Capri fisherman with his
net. 27,5 x 39,8 cm.

B271 The courtyard of the Franciscan monastery at Amalfi. 47,7 x
20,9 cm.

B272 A Franciscan monk, the her-
mit of the Colosseum in Rome. 32
x 22,2 cm.

B273 Half-length portrait of a
young Franciscan. Signed "E.
Meier". 26,8 x 22,2 cm.

Mohr, Johannes Georg Paul
Born Bordesholm, Holstein, 1808,
died Munich 1843.

B274 Winter landscape from Bordesholm. Signed "J. Mohr Kopen-
hagen 1840". 79,1 x 112,5 cm.

B275 Landscape from Ischldorf,
Bavaria. Signed "Mohr 1840". 81,1
x 118,3 cm.

Monaco, Lorenzo
Born Siena c. 1370, died Florence
c. 1425.

B1 The Virgin and Child. Tempera
on wood. 22,2 x 18,3 cm. Part of a
diptychon, the other part of which
is probably a St. Jerome in the
Rijksmuseum, Amsterdam, Inv. No.
1641 BI.

Monies, David
Born Copenhagen 1812, died ibid.
1894.

B418 Kitchen interior. Signed "D.
Monies 1861". 62,7 x 74,5 cm.
Purchased 1864.

Montanini, Pietro
Born Perugia 1625, died ibid. 1689.

B29 A tree struck by lightning. 65,4
x 49,1 cm. Attribution, formerly ascribed to Salvator Rosa.

Müller, Adam August
Born Copenhagen 1811, died ibid.
1844.

B276 Christ and The Evangelists.
Signed "Adam Müller Rom 1842".
251,1 x 156,9 cm.

Møller, Jens Peter
Born Faaborg 1783, died Copenhagen 1854.

B277 Landscape at Svendborg
Sound. Signed "J. P. M. 1843".
56,9 x 73,8 cm.

B278 The town of Svendborg, Funen. Signed "I. P. M. 1844". 48,7 x 71,9 cm.

Neergaard, Hermania Sigvardine
Born Copenhagen 1799, died Aldershvile, Bagsvœrd, 1875.

B279 Flowers in a glass. Signed "H. Neergaard 1842". 51 x 41,9 cm.

Nerly, Friedrich
Born Erfurt 1807, died Venice 1878.

B133 Buffaloes dragging a block of marble for Thorvaldsen through the Roman Campagna. Signed "F. Nerly fece". Replica of a painting from 1831 in Schwerin. 74,5 x 99,4 cm.

B402 Italian peasants at a fountain. Signed "Nerly". 40,5 x 50, 2 cm.

Oehme, Ernst Friedrich
Born Dresden 1797, died ibid. 1855.

B134 View of a Gothic church. Probably painted 1824 in Rome. 49,7 x 40,5 cm.

Onofri, Crescenzio
Born Rome 1632, died Florence 1698.

B31 Landscape. 95,5 x 139,3 cm. Attribution.
B32 Landscape. 95,5 x 139,3 cm. Attribution.

Oppenheim, Moritz
Born Hanau 1800, died Frankfurton-Main 1882.

B135 The return of Tobias. Signed "M. Oppenheim. Firenze MDCC-CXXIII". Painted on wood. 64,1 x 76,5 cm.

Orizonte,
See Bloemen, Jan Frans van.

Ottesen, Otto Diderich
Born Broager 1816, died Copenhagen 1892.

B280 Still life with fruit. Signed "O. D. Ottesen 1842". 28,2 x 36,6 cm.

B281 A luncheon table. Signed "O. D. Ottesen 1844". 39,2 X 33,4 cm.

Overbeck, Johann Friedrich
Born Lübeck 1789, died Rome 1869.

B136 The Virgin and Child. Painted on wood, 1818. 65,8 x 47,1 cm.

Dep. 3 The Good Shepherd. Painted on wood; probably in the 1860s. 36 x 24 cm. Lent by the Ny Carlsberg Glyptotek.

Pacetti, Michelangelo
Born Rome 1793, died after 1855.

B86 The Posillipo Grotto at Naples. Copy of a painting by G. B. Bassi. Probably 1833. 47,1 x 36,6 cm.

B401 View of the Tiber in Rome, showing St. Peter's and the Castle of St. Angelo. Signed "M. Pacetti Roma 1835". 41,5 x 54,5 cm.

Paggi, Giovanni Battista, after
B15 Venus and Cupid. Copy of a painting by G. B. Paggi in the

Palazzo Bianco, Genoa. Painted on copper. 10,9 x 9,1 cm.
Perugino, Pietro, after See Blunck B34.

Petzholdt. Ernst Christian Frederik (Fritz)
Born Copenhagen 1805, died Patras 1838.

B282 Landscape near Veii. Signed "F. Petzholdt. Roma 1835". 68 x 89,5 cm.

Pietrocola, Floriano
Born Vasto 1809, died Sorrento.

B426 Portrait of Thorvaldsen. Painted on paper. Oval. 14 x 11,5 cm. Presented to the Museum 1892.

Pinturicchio, School of
Italy, around 1500.

B5 The Virgin and Child. Copy of a painting by Pinturicchio in the National Gallery, Washington D. C., Cat.No. 141. Painted on wood. 36,6 x 27,5 cm.

Plagemann, Carl Gustav
Born Södertälje 1805, died Rome 1868.

B176 A nun in her cell. Signed "PL". Painted on wood. 44,8 X 36,6 cm.

Pontormo, Jacopo, after
B6 The Virgin and Child with the young St. John the Baptist. Copy of a painting by Pontormo in the Uffizi, Florence, Cat.No. 4347.

Painted on wood, probably in the late 18th or early 19th century. 109,9 x 86,3 cm.

Prestel, Johann Erdmann Gottlieb
Born Frankfurt-on-Main 1804, died Mainz 1885.

B137 Stag in a wood. Signed "J. G. Prestel Rom 1835". 74,5 x 99,8 cm.

Pseudo-Pier Francesco Fiorentino
Florence, late 15th century.

B3 Virgin and Child with two cherubs. Compare a painting ascribed to Pier Francesco Fiorentino in the National Gallery of Art, Washington (Kress Collection K402). Tempera on wood. 70,6 x 54,9 cm. Attribution.

Raphael, after
B303 Copy of a head in Raphael's fresco of "Heliodorus driven out of the Temple" in the Vatican. Painted on ivory. 3,9 x 5,2 cm.

B304 Copy of a head in Raphael's fresco of "Heliodorus driven out of the Temple" in the Vatican. Painted on ivory. 4,3 x 4,6 cm.

B305 Copy of a head in Raphael's fresco of "Heliodorus driven out of the Temple" in the Vatican. Painted on ivory. 4,7 x 4 cm.

See also: Blunck, D. C., B35; Eggers, C., B36; Eggink, J. L., B38; Cades, G., B39.

Rebell, Joseph
Born Vienna 1787, died Dresden
1828.

B138 The Isle of Capri Signed "Jos.
Rebell 1820". 45,1 x 66,7 cm.

Reinhart, Johann Christian
Born Hof 1761, died Rome 1847.

B139 Forest scene. Signed "C.
Reinhart ad nat. f. 1793". 73,2 x
98,1 cm.

B140 View of the gardens of the
Villa Borghese, Rome. Probably
painted 1793. 71,9 x 98,1 cm.

B141 View of the Ponte Lupo on
the River Anio near Tivoli, in the
foreground a youth playing the lyre.
Signed "C. Reinhart f. Roma
1823". Painted on wood. 38,6 x
52,3 cm.

Bl 42 Scene from the Roman Campagna, Torre del Quinto. Signed
"C. Reinhart Roma 1823". Painted
on wood. 47,7 x 63,4 cm.

B143 Italian landscape with a hun-
ter (self-portrait). Signed: "C. Reinhart Roma 1835". 45,1 x 58,8 cm.

Reinhold, Heinrich
Born Gera 1788, died Rome 1825.

B145 Landscape, with the Good
Samaritan. Signed "H. Reinhold
f. 1823". 38,6 x 52,3 cm.

B146 Landscape, with Hagar and
Ishmael. Signed "Reinhold f. 1823
Roma". 48,4 x 59,5 cm.

B147 View of St. Peter's from the
gardens of the Villa Doria Pamphili,
Rome. Signed "Reinhold f. 1823".
36,6 x 48,8 cm.

B413 Scene from the Isle of Capri.
Painted on wood, c. 1823. Unfinished. 47 x 66,3 cm.

Richardt, Carl Johan
Born Brede 1816, died Copenhagen
1887.

B283 Portrait of a sailor holding a
pipe. Signed "C. Richardt 1839".
62,8 x 49,1 cm.

Richardt, Joachim Ferdinand
Born Brede 1819, died Oakland,
California, 1895.

B284 A studio at the Academy of
Fine Arts, Copenhagen. Painted
c. 1839. 41,9 x 47,1 cm.

B285 Thorvaldsen in his studio at
the Academy of Fine Arts, Copenhagen. Signed "F. Richardt 1840".
44,5 x 57,5 cm.

Richter, Johann Heinrich
Born Coblenz 1803, died ibid.
1845.

B148 Portrait of the model Fortunata Segatori from Subiaco. Signed
"J. Richter f. Roma 1833". 74,5 x
62,8 cm.

B149 Roman woman with tambou-
rine. Signed "J. Richter f. Roma
1834". 68 x 56,2 cm.

Riedel, August
Born Bayreuth 1799, died Rome
1883.

B150 A Neapolitan fisherman and
his family. Signed "A. Riedel 1833".
75,9 x 100,7 cm.

B151 Girl bathing. Signed"Riedel f. 1837". 65,4 x 47,1 cm.

Riepenhausen, Johannes
Born Göttingen 1789, died Rome 1860.

B152 Venus and Adonis. Signed "J. Riepenhausen". 81,7 x 61,5 cm.

B153 Cupid instructing two young girls. 62,2 x 49,7 cm.

B154 Bramante presenting Raphael to Pope Julius II. Signed "J. Riepenhausen". Probably painted 1836. 49,7 x 62,2 cm.

B155 A second-hand bookseller in a Roman street, in the background. the Temple of Mars Ultor and the Arco di Pantano. Signed "J. Riepenhausen". 49,1 x 66,2 cm.

Robert, Léopold
Born La Chaux-de-Fonds 1794, died Venice 1835.

B92 The Church of San Paolo fuori le mura the day after the fire of 1823. Replica of a painting from 1824 in the Musee d'Art et d'Histoire, Neuchâtel. Signed »L¹ᵈ Robert Roma 1825«. 102 x 82,4

B93 A young Greek sharpening his dagger. Signed »L¹ᵈ Robert Roma 1829«. 49,1 x 41,9cm.

Roed, Jørgen
Born Ringsted 1808, died Copenhagen 1888.

B417 Portrait of the painter Albert Küchler (Fra Pietro). Signed "Albert Küchler". Malet i Rom 1862 af J. Roed. 59,5 x 46,7 cm. Presented to the Museum 1863.

Romanelli, Giovanni Francesco (?)
Born Viterbo c. 1610, died ibid. 1662.

B28 Apollo wearing a laurel wreath. 68 x 49,7 cm. A very tentative attribution.

Rubby, John James
Born Plymouth 1750, died Rome 1812.
See Catel, B299.

Rugendas, Johann Moritz
Born Augsburg 1802, died Weilheim 1858.

B302 Tropical landscapc (South America?) by moonlight. 22,2 x 30,8 cm. Attribution.

Rørbye, Martinus Christian
Born Drammen 1803, died Copenhagen 1848.

B286 View of Athens from the south-west. Signed "Athen M. Rørbye 1836". 51 x 78,5 cm.

B287 Harbour scene. Palermo. Signed "M. Rørbye 1844". 83,7 x 125,5 cm.

Salvi, Giovanni Battista (Sassoferrato)
Born Sassoferrato 1609, died Rome 1685.

B16 Praying Virgin. 49,1 x 37,2 cm. Presented to Thorvaldsen by Pope Pius VII.

Sassoferrato,
See Salvi, Giovanni Battista

Scarsella, Ippolito (Scarsellino), after

B12 A halt during the Flight into Egypt. Copy of a painting ascribed to Scarsellino in the Galleria Nazionale, Parma, Cat.No. 374. Painted on copper. 29,4 x 24,1 cm.

Schack, Sophus Peter Lassenius
Born Copenhagen 1811, died ibid. 1864.

B288 Children singing in a courtyard, winter Signed "S. S. 1838". 36,5 x 29,2 cm.

Schadow, Wilhelm
Born Berlin 1788, died Düsseldorf 1862.

B156 The Road to Calvary. Painted on wood. 30,1 x 41,9 cm.

Schedoni,
see Schidone, Bartolomeo

Schick, Gottlieb
Born Stuttgart 1776, died ibid. 1812.

B157 Heroic landscape, with Hagar and Ishmael (?). Probably painted 1803-04. 87,6 x 116,4cm.

B158 Heroic landscape, with Ruth and Boas. The landscape in the middle distance and background is the work of J. A. Koch. Probably painted 1803-04. 87,6 x 116,4 cm.

Schidone, Bartolomeo, after
B43 The Virgin and Child with the young St. John the Baptist. Copy of a painting by Schidone in the collection of Denis Mahon, London. 47,1 x 35,3 cm.

Schilbach, Johann Heinrich
Born Barchfeld a.d. Werra 1798, died Darmstadt 1851.

B159 View of the Forum Romanum towards the Capitol. Signed "J. H. Schilbach Rom 1825". 45,1 x 60,2 cm.

B160 View from the Capitol, looking towards the Forum Romanum. Signed "H. Schilbach Roma 18(26)". 46,5 x 60,8 cm.

Schleisner, Christian Andreas
Born Lyngby 1810, died Copenhagen 1882.

B289 A shoemaker's shop, apprentices poking fun at their master. Signed "C. Schleisner 1838". 58,8 x 51,7 cm.

Schorn, J.
Active at the beginning of the 19th century.

B446 Portrait of Count Wlodzimierz Potocki. Signed "Schorn Pinxit". Gouache. 20,1 x 17 cm.

Seidler, Louise
Born Jena 1786, died Weimar 1866.

B440 Portrait of Fanny Caspars.
Signed "Luise S.". Painted 1819. 74
x 60,5 cm. Presented to the Museum 1937.

Senff, Adolf
Born Halle 1785, died Ostrau
1863.

B161 An antique terracotta vase
with flowers. Signed "Adolfo Senff.
1828". 47,1 x 36,6 cm.

Severn, Joseph
Born Hoxton 1793, died Rome
1879.

B99 Italian woman and her daughter. Signed "I. Severn Rome 1831".
75,2 x 62,8 cm.

B100 Vintage scene, Italy. Painted
on wood, c. 1824. 40,5 x 35,5 cm.

Skovgaard, Peter Christian
Born Hammershus near Ringsted
1817, died Copenhagen 1875.

B450 Nysø on a clear autumn day.
Signed "PSkovgaard-1853". 74 x
112 cm. Bequeathed to the Museum by Rigmor Stampe and Astrid
Stampe Feddersen and presented
1974.

Smith, Ludvig August
Born Copenhagen 1820, died ibid.
1906.

B290 The painter J. V. Gertner in
his room. Painted c. 1840. 55,2 x
49,7 cm.

Sonne, Jørgen Valentin
Born Birkerød 1801, died Copenhagen 1890.

B291 A battlefield on the morning
after the battle. Signed "I. V. Sonne
1833". 59,5 x 79,8 cm.

B292 Roman country people outside the osteria at Ponte Mammolo.
Signed I". Sonne Roma 1835". 41,9
x 57,5 cm.

B443 Portrait of Thorvaldsen. Trial
section for the frieze on the facade
of the Museum. Coloured plaster,
c. 1846. 58,8 x 63,6 cm.
Purchased 1938.

Steingrübel, Joseph
Born Augsburg 1804, died ibid.
1838.

B162 View of Florence. Signed
"J. Steingrübel pinx. Firenze 1834".
43,2 x 53,6 cm.

Stern, Ignaz
Born Mariahilf c. 1680, died Rome
1748.

B55 Boy blowing soap bubbles.
Painted on wood. 60,2 x 94,2 cm.

Stieler, Joseph Karl
Born Mainz 1781, died Munich
1858.

B163 Portrait of Ludwig I of Bavaria. Painted c. 1822. 70 x 51,7 cm.

Storelli, Felix Maria Fernando
Born Turin 1778, died Paris 1854.

B85 Italian landscape. Signed "F^d Storelli 1833". 52,9 x 74,5 cm.

Suhrlandt, Rudolph
Born Ludwigslust 1781, died Schwerin 1862.

B422 Portrait of Thorvaldsen. Replica of B428, painted 1810. 61,5 x 48,5 cm. Purchased by the Museum 1881.

B423 Portrait of Antonio Canova. Painted c. 1812. 62 x 49 cm. Purchased by the Museum 1881.

B428 Portrait of Thorvaldsen. Signed "R. Suhrlandt pin. 1810". 61,9 x 49 cm. Presented to the Museum 1921.

Taddeo di Bartolo
Born Siena 1362/63, died ibid. 1422.

B2 Predella with, from left to right: Mary Magdalene, Christ in Gethsemane, The Crucifixion, The Resurrection, St. Catherine of Alexandria. Probably painted between 1400 and 1405. Tempera on wood. 17,7 x 145,1 cm.

Teerlink, Abraham
Born Dordrecht 1776, died Rome 1857.

B102 Landscape with cattle. Signed "Teerlink f.". 30,1 x 41,9.

B103 Italian landscape. Painted on wood. 35,3 x 48,4 cm.

Thöming, Ferdinand Christian Friedrich
Born Eckernförde 1802, died Naples 1873.

B293 A Danish corvette. Signed "Thöming". 28,2 x 36,6 cm.

B294 American brig at anchor in the Bay of Naples. Signed »Thöming pinx. Napoli 1827". 49,7 x 77,2 cm.

B295 The Bay of Naples. Thorvaldsen and Thöming are seated in the nearest fishing-boat with other travellers. Signed "Sorent 1828. F. Thöming". 51 x 75,9 cm.

B296 View of the coast of Capri near Marina Piccola. Signed "F. Thöming pinx. 1829". 45,8 X 80,5 cm.

B297 The Blue Grotto, Capri. Signed "Thöming pinx. 1833". 13,1 x 21,5 cm.

B298 Surf at the coast of Capri. 43,2 x 58,8 cm.

Tischbein, Carl Wilhelm
Born Dessau 1797, died Bückeburg 1855.

B164 Neapolitan fisherman's daughter. Painted between 1816 and 1818. 61,5 x 52,3 cm.

Titian,
See Tiziano Vecellio

Tiziano Vecellio, after

B18 The Virgin and Child with the young St. John the Baptist. Copy of a painting ascribed to the School of Titian in the Uffizi, Florence, Cat. No. 967. Painted on copper. 21,5 x 17 cm.

B40 The education of Cupid. Copy of a painting by Titian in the Galleria Borghese, Rome, Inv. No. 170. 119 x 189,6 cm.

B41 Reclining Venus. Reduced copy of a painting "Venus from Urbino", by Titian in the Uffizi, Florence, Cat. No. 1437. 25,5 x 31,4 cm.

Törmer, Benno Friedrich
Born Dresden 1804, died Rome 1859.

B403 Woman from Procida. Signed "Toermer Rom 1833". 34 x 46,7 cm.

Venetian School
16th century.

B11 Portrait of a Lady. 74,5 x 60,2 cm

Vernet, Horace
Born Paris 1789, died ibid. 1863.

B94 Portrait of an Armenian priest. Signed "HVt 1830". 62,2 x 50 cm.

B95 Portrait of Thorvaldsen modelling the bust of Vernet. Signed "Horace Vernet à Son Illustre ami Torwaldsen Rome 1833". 99,8 x 75,2 cm.

Verschuir, Lieve
Born c. 1630, died Rotterdam 1686.

B48 Seascape. Signed "L. V." Painted on wood. 17,7 x 22,9 cm. Attribution.

Verstappen, Martin
Born Antwerp 1773, died Rome 1853.

B104 A roadside chapel between Albano and Ariccia. 35,3 x 48,4 cm.

Vogel von Vogelstein, Carl Christian
Born Wildenfels 1788, died Munich 1868.

B425 Portrait of Thorvaldsen. Signed on the back "Carl Vogel pinx. Roma 1815". 108 x 78,5 cm. Purchased 1890.

Voogd, Hendrik
Born Amsterdam 1766, died Rome 1839.

B56 Italian landscape. 25,5 x 37,2 cm. Attribution.

Wächter, Eberhard
Born Balingen 1762, died Stuttgart 1852.

B165 Portrait of the painter J. A. Koch. Painted between 1795 and 1798. 29,4 x 22,9 cm.

Weller, Theodor Leopold
Born Mannheim 1802, died ibid. 1880.

B166 Street performers in the Piazza Montanara, Rome. Signed "18 TW29 Roma". 69,3 x 88,3 cm.

West, William Edward
Born Lexington, Kentucky, 1788, died Nashville 1857.

B449 Portrait of Thorvaldsen. 68,5 x 55,5 cm. Presented to the Museum 1972.

Westphal, Friederich (Fritz)
Born Schleswig 1804, died Copenhagen 1844.

B453 The Reception of Thorvaldsen on Toldboden in Copenhagen, the 17th of September 1838. Painted between 1839 and 1841. 71,5 x 100 cm.

Williams, Penry
Born Merthyr Tydfil 1802, died Rome 1885.

B101 A shepherd-boy and a girl the Roman Campagna, in the background Aqua Claudia. Signed "Penry Williams Rome 1842". 78,5 X 61,5 cm.

Wittmer, Johann Michael
Born Murnau 1802, died Munich 1880.

B167 Æsop seated on a plinth above a spring, telling his fables to the people. Signed "M. Wittmer F. Romœ 1841". 73,2 X 107,9 cm.

Zeuthen, Christian Olavius
Born Kastrup 1812, died Copenhagen 1890.

B431 The courtyard of the Thorvaldsen Museum. Signed "Zeuthen. 1847". Painted on paper. 19,9 X 25,5 cm. Purchased 1924.

Thorvaldsen and Antiquity

Thorvaldsen's fervent preoccupation with Classical Antiquity manifested itself in many areas. First of all, it had a deep impact upon his own work as an artist. It also influenced the ways in which he discharged his official duties, e.g. as professor at the San Luca Academy in Rome, and as the restorer of classical sculpture for the Vatican and for Crown Prince Ludvig's Glyptothek in Munich. In addition, Thorvaldsen purchased Greek and Roman objects of art on behalf of others, and he frequently served as an adviser in conjunction with such purchases.

Thorvaldsen spent nearly forty years in Rome (1797–1838). The city was a major centre for archaeological research as well as for art dealers and collectors, providing him with a major impetus to build up a collection of his own that amounted to almost 10,000 objects. At the same time his ever-growing absorption in the process of collecting had a distinct influence on his attitude towards contemporary art and aesthetics.

When he returned to Copenhagen in 1838, Thorvaldsen brought his collection with him, donating it to the museum that was to be built to house both his own work and his collections of items from Classical Antiquity.

Prior to this, the collection was located in Thorvaldsen's apartment in Casa Buti on the Via Sistina in Rome, close to the Spanish Steps. Amid his archaeological specimens, Thorvaldsen was in day-to-day contact with the ancient world - to the extent that Thorvaldsen very often had to move the objects around in order to get to his things or to provide visitors with a seat, according to eye-witness descriptions of his apartment.

This decidedly private nature still enshrouds Thorvaldsen's collection of works from Antiquity, and explains much of its unique charm. Although the particular circumstances of time, place and the people involved will often limit the scope of any particular collection, it is also true that the very charm and sense of intimacy of such a collection often depends on this very set of circumstances. Thorvaldsen's collection includes items that the artist acquired either because of a spontaneous interest in a specific piece or because he thought that the item might provide him with the solution to a problem of shape or motif that he was preoccupied with.

The architect M. G. Bindesbøll aimed at retaining this sense of privacy and intimacy when designing the display cases and planning the presentation of the archaeological items for the future Thorvaldsen Museum (inaugurated in 1848). The decorative scheme remains virtually unaltered to this very day. The exhibition thus still features a little of the 'confused disarray' that one visitor found so characteristic of Thorvaldsen's collection of antiquities when seeing it in the artist's Roman apartment.

Most of the items in the collection stem from contemporary archaeological excavations in southern Italy and on Sicily, in Etruria (in the central part of Italy) and in Egypt. Thorvaldsen also purchased artefacts from antique dealers in Rome and from peasant farmers who came into the city on market days and peddled whatever finds they had made while tilling their fields. Because of this, the exact locations where most of the items in Thorvaldsen's collection of Antiquity were found are unfortunately unknown.

THE EGYPTIAN COLLECTION

Thorvaldsen acquired most, if not all, of his Egyptian collection in 1826, which was relatively late in his stay. Most of the items originated from contemporary excavations in Egypt itself but some of the items were undoubtedly found in Italy (in Etruria, Pompeii and Herculaneum, for example). The Egyptian finds stem solely from burials, mainly from the seventh century B.C. and onwards to the

Greek-Roman period (the third century B.C. the third/fourth century A.D). A few individual items can also be dated to the second millennium B.C.

Cases 3 contains hundreds of amulets depicting figures of gods or other symbolic representations intended to protect the deceased or certain particular parts of his/her body. On the upper shelf there are also larger statuettes of gods, mainly Osiris in mummy form and the enthroned Isis suckling the Horus child.

Case 4 contains stone vessels, mostly made of alabaster, for creams and perfumes. In *case 5* there are bright strings of beads and rings made of so called faience, which is in fact a material containing a large proportion of quartz and whose surface thus becomes vitrified when fired. *Case 6* includes a display of wooden items from the second millennium B.C., such as a spoon for ointments which is shaped like a human hand holding a mussel shell. The double box with a swing lid and makeup stick is for use with kohl eye makeup. The female figure is a depiction of a slave woman clad in a long dresslike costume and with her hair set up in thick plaits. The bronze items include a mirror with an impression of the linen bag the mirror was kept in, transfixed in the verdigris surface of the bronze.

Case 7 features displays of various depictions of the deceased person, sometimes in a kneeling posture bearing a figure of a god (356-57) or a stele on which a prayer to the sun god to preserve the bearer's face undamaged is inscribed (354-55). There are also numerous so-called "ushabti" figures, usually in mummy form. These were to assist the deceased in performing the ritual acts which were obligatory for the deceased when in the kingdom of the dead.

The freestanding deskstyle showcases display various kinds of mummy collars and other forms of mummy decoration, painted in vibrant colours on a plaster base. There are also large scarabs, which were placed alongside the mummy near the deceased's heart as a form of protection.

Below these showcases are a series of canopic urns made of alabaster. In those were the inner organs of the deceased, they were protected by the divinities, the four sons of Osiris, whose heads in pictorial form serve as lids.

The stele above the showcase to the right dates from the twelfth century B.C. and depicts Pa-ger-ger standing in the entrance to the burial chamber. The inscription declares that Pa-ger-ger was a prominent engraver, and also prays that things go well for him on the journey into the kingdom of the dead.

The books on display here and those in the next room, room 36, are part of Thorvaldsen´s library. The bulk of these books are works with an archaeological content.

METAL, IVORY, BONE AND GLASS ITEMS

The objects in this room stem from Greece, Etruria and Rome. They show everyday life via the chores, personal care and cult habits of their users.

BRONZES

The many statuettes in *Case 1* come from items such as vessels and jugs for instance the satyr (8) and the youth (17), which are Etruscan masterpieces from the early fifth century B.C. and the late fourth century B.C. respectively. The figures dancing on their toes with drinking horns in one raised hand and sacrificial bowls in the other (62-65) depict the Roman house gods called the Lares, which were placed on the altar in each house. The statuettes of Jupiter (34), Ceres (36), Mars (40), Venus (41) and Hercules (69) can also stem from house altars as they are known from Pompeii, among other places.

The group that depicts two lions tearing an antelope apart (29, *case 2*) was once the handle to a magnificent footbath vessel, probably made in Athens, from c. 500 B.C.

Etruscan mirrors from c. 500 B.C. to the second century B.C. are on display in *Case 4*. Bronze is an excellent reflective material when highly polished. Glass mirrors were known in Antiquity, but never became particularly widespread. The convex front of the metal mirror provided a smaller image but more overall views. The reverse of such mirrors were often decorated with engraved representations of gods and heroes.

Case 7 shows the special version of the Etruscan candelabrum (306), where tallow candles were fixed on with their sides pressed in over the horizontal spikes that encircle the top figure. In this case, it is an athlete engaged in cleaning off oils and dust by using a bath scraper, two examples of which hang on the right hand side of the showcase.

In *case 8* is a sphinx handle from a large wine vessel (280) and a jug handle shaped like a youth with lions and rams resting at his shoulders and feet (273). These are bronze masterpieces from an Etruscan workshop of the early fifth century B.C. and a workshop in Sparta from c. 520 B.C.

IVORY AND BONE *(case 9)*
SILVER AND GLASS *(cases 11-12)*

The fragmented ivory head depicts Serapis, the EgyptianGreek god of the underworld. The jointed doll is a toy of a kind sometimes found in graves of young girls from the second and third centuries A.D. The silver head in *case 11* depicts a Roman from the middle of the second century A.D. This head may have been the central decoration in a silver bowl. Prominent among the faience and glass objects of Greek and Roman manufacture, respectively, is the polychrome semispherical glass bowl. This kind of work, formed from pieces of glass rods melted together into a shape, dates from the first century A.D. and was very much sought after.

GOLD *(case 13)*

The museum's collection of gold jewellery contains excellent examples of how the craftsmen of antiquity were masters at mounting gold wire and gold balls on a sheet gold base in intricate patterns of leaves and figures. The Etruscan ear stud jewellery (68-69, 70-71 and 72) deserve particular attention. The pendant with a flint arrowhead mounted in gold is an Etruscan amulet. The pieces of flint were supposed to have come from the lightning of the god Tinias, and were thought to be capable of warding off evil. 55-60 are amulet capsules, where the vases haped and round ones are Etruscan and the other two are Roman. A copy of no. 56 is on sale in the museum shop.

GEMS AND CAMEOS

Thorvaldsen's collection of signets and ornamental stones was probably the dearest of all his possessions from Antiquity. Thorvaldsen himself was often quoted as saying things indicating this, and it was a point of view widely shared by his contemporaries. It was clearly considered an honour on the occasions when the Scandinavians in Rome held their traditional celebrations on the evening before Christmas Day and Thorvaldsen offered seven or eight gems as prizes in the obligatory lottery run on that occasion.

GEMS

Gemma is the Latin word for pearls and precious stones. Today the word is commonly used for semiprecious stones with a motif inscribed and set in a ring made of gold, silver or iron. The collection contains examples of all three materials, but it should be noted that most of the gold rings are rings made in Thorvaldsen's time as mountings for gems that were considered particularly valuable or interesting.

The precious stones most commonly used were cornelian, agate, sard, nicolo, plasma and jasper. After Alexander the Great's campaign in the Orient at the end of the fourth century B.C. exotic stones such as garnet, lapis lazuli, amethyst, onyx and quartz came into circulation. In Roman times glass copies of such stones were also common, sometimes involving colour compositions that do not exist in nature. In technical terms, it must be pointed out how remarkable these gems, considering that magnifying glasses were not used in the engraving work, as they were not known in Antiquity.

The engraved stones were usually intended for putting the owner's seal on something ("signing" it with a "signet" ring), which is why the motifs used are frequently engraved as mirror images in order to form a correct impression. "Signing" was used a lot in Antiquity, both on dispatches of all kinds so that the recipient could see that the dispatch had arrived from the sender without being opened, and on seals used on cupboards, chests, caskets and other similar household items, which the house owner would use his signet ring to seal.

The engraved stones could also serve as amulets, with special motifs engraved depicting such entities as Fortuna, the goddess of fortune, or animals such as the scorpion to wield off evil, or imaginary compositions of humans and animals. Precious stones were also considered healthgiving in themselves, each one influencing a particular area of the body. Quite naturally, the signet and amulet functions often became mixed together, and the stones and their engravings were also considered jewellery.

Most of the gems are from the period between the third century B.C. and the second and third centuries A.D. The Etruscan scarabs are a special group (*case 1,* on the right) with their carvings on the plane base of the scarab. Almost without exception these were carved in cornelian, the stone most commonly used for gems, and date from the sixth to the first centuries B.C.

CAMEOS

In contrast to gems, cameos (see the lower rows in *case 3,* on the left) are carved in positive relief and have thus not been used to "sign" with, but solely as items of jewellery.

The same kinds of stone are generally used for cameos as for gems, but composite stones with two or three different alternating light and dark layers were especially in demand. These characteristics were used to highlight the individual features in a motif, such as the background, the flesh and the clothing of the figures.

THE GREEK COINS

Greek coins from sixth to the second centuries B.C. are noteworthy among the coins of Antiquity, and this is particularly true of those originating from Sicily. These are among the very best examples of the art of minting coins to be found anywhere in the world. Thorvaldsen must have been exceedingly careful about the quality, as he managed to put together so beautiful and representative a collection of this wonderful type of coins (see *cases 1 and 2* on the left going in).

MATERIALS, TECHNIQUES AND MOTIFS

The materials most commonly used for coins were silver and bronze, although gold was also used. The coins were produced using die-stamping, where a heated and weighed clump of metal was placed over a lower (obverse) die bearing a motif engraved as a mirror image. The uppermost (reverse) die was also engraved with a negative image, and when this striking surface struck the metal in the minting process the lower die formed the coin's flat while the upper die formed the reverse with the characteristic raised edge. In other words it is the shape of the coin's faces that indicate the obverse and reverse of the Greek coins, not the motifs used, as in the coins we know today.

Among the motifs that were common on classical Greek coins were one of the town's divinities or a local demigod of special importance, on the one face, and a reference to some particular product that the town was known for such as olives, wine, corn, etc. on the other. The possible combinations were innumerable.

In Athens the basic type of coin was made of silver, weighed about 4 grams, and was called the drachm, forerunner of the modern Greek drachma. On the face is the head of Athene wearing a helmet, and on the reverse side an owl and an olive branch (*case 1* to the left, A 42-45). There were also 2,4 (A 36-41) and 10 drachm coins. At the other end of the range was the obol (A 46), which was worth 1/6 of a drachm, and also halfobol (A 47-48) and quarterobol coins (A 54). A building worker working on the Acropolis in Athens was paid one drachm a day c. 400 B.C., and a citizen received the same amount for sitting in the people's assembly for one day.

Thorvaldsen's Sicilian coins include a 4 drachm coin from the town of Naxos on the east coast of Sicily (*case 1* to the left, A180), a coin of the best possible quality. The motif on the reverse is a lustful satyr (a human with the ears, tail and hooves of a horse) sitting on the ground and greeting the onlooker with a cup of wine in his lifted hand. The letters around him tell that it is a coin belonging to the NAXIANS. It is astounding how direct and at the same time monumental a picture has been created in a miniature only 2.8 centimetres in diameter.

Other outstanding Sicilian 4 drachm coins include A 181 from Katane with the local river god on the obverse, and A 184 and A 185 from Leontini, one featuring a carriage for racing with a fourinhand and driver garlanded by the goddess of victory, and the other a female head surrounded by four ears of corn (Demeter?) on the reverse. There is also a 4 drachm coin (A 194) from Syracuse, with the head of Arethusa, the local river goddess, surrounded by a drawing of a circle and four dolphins playing.

The Greek citystates had learned the art of minting coins from Lydia in western Turkey, and knowledge of the techniques involved now spread to the whole of the Mediterranean world, including Gaul (*centre case on the right*). The Romans (*case 1* on the right, nearest the doorway) learned about the minting of coins from the Greek towns in southern Italy when the Roman expansion reached that far in the third century B.C.

MARBLE AND TERRACOTTA

One might well expect that a sculptor collecting pieces from Antiquity would aim at acquiring a collection of sculpture that was somewhat larger than is the case with Thorvaldsen´s. The explanation is probably quite a simple one, he thought that the market price was too high. Several people who had been advised by Thorvaldsen on the purchase of ancient sculpture mentioned that he held such views. However, a closer examination of his collection reveals many excellent and interesting pieces, with fine samples of considerable craftsmanship, which a professional like Thorvaldsen would be able to appreciate, since this made a good fragment of more value than a whole sculpture of poorer quality.

MARBLE

One eminent example of good craftsmanship is the marble hair and ear fragment (50) on *the top shelf of the showcase on the left.* This little section is in itself sufficient to show that the sculpture to which it originally belonged was perhaps the best Roman copy of one of the famous fifth century B.C. athlete sculptures made by the Greek sculptor Polycleitos.

The portrait of a boy *on top of the showcase* is from the second century A.D. and is an expressive piece of work from a period that has given us what are probably the best child portraits known from Antiquity. The head beside it is a copy of a portrait statue of the Greek speaker, Demosthenes, the original of which once stood on the Agora in Athens. By far the majority of the stone sculptures are either full or reduced size copies of Greek works from the fifth century B.C. and later, used by the Romans to decorate both public and private rooms.

TERRACOTTA

The enthroned figures of gods and their standing worshippers in the showcase to the right mostly originate from Greek shrines and burial sites in southern Italy and on Sicily. The bottommost shelf displays small transportable domestic altars and a large phallos to ward off evil, it may have been placed at the entrance to a house. Most of the heads on the upper shelf, on the top of the showcase and on the shelf above the desk showcase were once set up in Etruscan shrines or fixed on Etruscan buildings as decorative and protective tiles.

The desk showcase contains mainly a large collection of Roman oil lamps. These worked with a lighted wick in the hole in the nozzle and were the most common form of artificial light in homes at that time. The many motifs used are derived just as much from the world of the gods as from everyday life, including scenes from the circus and gladiator contests in the arenas of the town, and a mouse engaged in gorging itself on the rich lamp oil.

The large tablets leaning against the base of the showcase show Herakles, one the heroes in Greek myths and legends, in his struggle with the Lion, the manyheaded monster Hydra, and the Cretan bull. These tablets originate from a shrine in either central or southern Italy. The many fragments that Bindesbøll, the architect who designed the museum, built into the wall as a form of collage *above the* desk showcase come from tablets decorated with figures, which have served various decorative purposes. They can be dated from the first century B.C. to the first century A.D.

POTTERY FROM CLASSICAL ANTIQUITY

The majority of the pottery featuring decorative figures on display here was made in Greece but found in Italy, where a comprehensive import of Greek vases took place over several centuries. Most were undoubtedly found during excavations of the southern Etruscan towns, which were begun in the 1820s. Thorvaldsen had at that time both the necessary means and an interest in purchasing vases, and made the most of his opportunity.

Gottlieb Bindesbøll, the architect, put the greatest emphasis on the motifs used on the vases when displaying them in the museum. The idea was that the exhibition should serve as a gallery of pictures from Antiquity, corresponding to the museum's gallery of paintings.

THE DIFFERENT GROUPS OF POTTERY

The upper shelves of cases 1 and 2 on the left and on the right contain blackfigure pottery from Athens and Corinth (*case 1, uppermost shelf on the left*) from the sixth century B.C. The lower shelf in *case 1* contains mainly socalled "bucchero" black burned pottery from Etruria (sixth and fifth centuries B.C.), while the pottery on *the lower shelf of case 2* comes from southern Italy and Etruria (fourth to the second centuries B.C.). *Cases 3 and 4* contain redfigure pottery, with pottery from Athens (fifth and sixth centuries B.C.) on the upper shelves and pottery from southern Italy and Etruria (fourth century B.C.) on the lower shelves.

TECHNIQUE

The black and red colours that are so characteristic for decorated pottery from this period come about as a result of the technique used in firing the vases. When they are fired using normal levels of oxygen the oxygen reacts with the iron content of the clay and colours the clay red. The oxygen flow is then interrupted and the whole vase becomes coloured black. A thin layer of clay containing potassium is brushed on before firing to make sure that the sections that are to remain black are not reoxidised to red when the oxygen flow is resumed. The fact that the Corinthian pottery (*case 1, uppermost shelf on the left*) is lighter is due to the lower iron content of the clay used.

DECORATION

Many of the motifs used in the blackfigure pottery from Athens depict gods and heroes. Considering that the pottery was primarily for serving wine, it is natural that Dionysus, the god of wine, and his accompanying satyrs and nympfs figure so prominently on these vases. Among the labours of Herakles (*case 1 on the left, shelf 2*) Herakles can be seen stuffing a boar into the storage jar where the king who had ordered the animal's capture is hiding.

There are also god and hero motifs in the redfigure pottery, such as the drinking cup (*case 4, shelf 2*) decorated with scenes from the Iliad, including Aphrodite fleeing after having been wounded by the Greek hero Diomedes, by the pot painter Oltos. But at the same time everyday scenes were becoming more popular. The drinking cups uppermost against the rear panel of *case 4*, painted by the socalled Foundry Painter and the Brygos Painter, depict scenes from the sports arena. The youth with a yoke bearing two baskets on the inner surface of the cup (*case 3, shelf 2 on the left*) probably shows Greek pottery painting at its best. The scene with a youth, purse in hand, visiting one of Athens´ prostitutes (*case 3, upper shelf, centre*) was painted by the Penthesilea Painter.

Illustrations

List of illustrations

3

4

5

6

7

8

9

10

12

14

15

16

17

18

19

ECKERSBERG

PITTORE

23

24

25

27

28

29

30

31

32

33

34

35

36

38

39

41

45

46

47

48

49

50

51

52

53

54

55

56

57

58

59

60

61

63

64

65

66

THORVALDSENS ANKOMST OG MODTAGELSE PAA KIØBENHAVNS RHED DEN 17 SEPT. 1838.

67

68

69

70

71

72

73

74

75

76

77

78

79

80

81

82

83

84

85

86

87

88

89

90

91

92

93

94

95

96A

96B

97

99

Index

Thorvaldsen's works (titles abridged)